The
Fire Brigade Hand
Special Appliances - Volume 2

The Fire Brigade Handbook - Special Appliances - Volume 2

The Fire Brigade Handbook - Special Appliances Volume 2 - is a directory of fire appliances manufactured for use by the various fire authorities in England, Scotland and Wales and follows on from the much acclaimed Handbook of current fire brigade appliances also published by British Bus Publishing. The form describes the fleet number, registration and type, together with the most recent station to which it was allocated. Invariably appliances move from time to time to meet the demands placed on the brigades.

This is the first of two volumes dedicated to the special appliances such as turntable ladders, emergency tenders and covers production details from the rare to the numerous of each type under the chassis class.

Obtaining the comprehensive information for this book has been a major task. This is the first attempt at publishing a pair of books of its type and covers specialist appliances from the early 1920's. In a lot of cases very little information is available so I have had to accept some information in good faith, and I have made it as accurate as I have been able to ascertain. I therefore would welcome any additional information and photographic material which would help in future publications.

Principal Editor: Clive Shearman

Acknowledgments:
I am grateful to the invaluable assistance of a number of people in the preparation of this publication . The Late Alan Batchelor, Mike Bunn, Norman Downs, Les Edkins, Roy Goodey , Ron Henderson, The Late John Hughes, Michael Lawmon, David Mitchell, Ian Moore, Ken Reid, Steve Shaw, David Thomas and Keith Wardell for the use of their excellent photographic and slide collections. Finally special mention for Ron Henderson and Ian Moore, who both did hundreds of hours of proof reading and gave valuable advice, assistance and encouragement

ISBN 1 897990 49 9 (Volume 1)
ISBN 1 897990 50 2 (Volume 2)

Published by *British Bus Publishing* Ltd
The Vyne, 16 St Margarets Drive, Wellington,
Telford, Shropshire, TF1 3PH
© British Bus Publishing, December 1997

Frontispiece: **City of Norwich Fire Brigade's ERF Hydraulic Platform JCL999G was delivered to the Bethel Street station in 1968. It served for 14 years before the Simon SS70 booms were remounted onto a Dennis F125 low line chassis. The machine was then based at Great Yarmouth, by then part of the Norfolk Fire Service.** *Ian Moore*

CONTENTS

KEY

Reg No	Fleet No	TYPE	YR	OS	BRIGADE	Details/Stations
Example						
700EJF	**TL9**	**TL**	**62**	**84**	**City of Leicester**	**#1 Lancaster Place - Central-1974** **SD30 Lancaster Place - Central** **Leicestershire Fire Service** **Haydon-Magirus-100 L**

Reg No						
Reg No						
700EJF						Vehicle Registration Number
	Fleet No Ladder Type					
	TL9 **MW/MZ** **MG No**					Vehicle Fleet or Code Number Merryweather Ladder Production No Magirus/Metz Ladder Number
		Type				
		TL				Type of Appliance-Turntable Ladder See Appliance Code List
			YR			
			62			Year put into service-1949
				OS		
				84		Year taken out of service-1969
					BRIGADE	
					City of Leicester	Original purchasing Brigade/City/ County Borough. These ceased to exist in the England & Wales in 1974. In Scotland the changeover took place in 1975.
						Details/Station
						Lancaster Place, Leicester was the original allocation for this vehicle. In 1974 it became **SD30** (the station code number). Central of the Leicestershire Fire Service. Some machines will have the letters **Re-ch** (Re-chassied). This applies to earlier bodies/ladders/booms etc being put onto later chassis types.

AUSTIN

Reg No	Fleet No Home Office Reference No	TYPE	YR	OS	Appliance & Brigade Name	Details/Stations
					Austin K4 Merryweather 60' Turntable Ladders	The War Department placed a large order for TL's. The K4 was a 5 ton machine ideally suited to mounting a ladder on. The type chosen was a 3 stage manually operated 60' Merryweather, fitted with stabilizing jacks. When delivered the GXN series were not fitted with pumps. Barton front mounted pumps were fitted at a later date.
GXN201	1	TLP	43	71	Shrewsbury (Shropshire)	Shrewsbury-1958/St Michael's St-Shrewsbury-1971 Shropshire FB
GXN202	2	TLP	43	59	Kent-Faversham (South East)	Old Dover Rd-Canterbury-1946 / DD-King St-Margate-1959 Kent Fire Brigade
GXN203	3	TLP	43	65	Cornwall	A1 St Georges Rd-Truro-Cornwall CFB-1948 N02 Ilfracombe-Devon CFB-1965 **Ladder Re-chassied onto Bedford TK-CTA298C**
GXN204	4	TLP	43	54	Leeds City (West Yorkshire)	City of Leeds Fire Stations-Sold 1954
GXN205	5	TLP	44 ?	65	Essex-Brentwood	North Rd-Brentwood-1946 / Bridgewater Fire Station-1965 Somerset Fire Brigade
GXN206	6	TLP	44 ?	66	Hampshire	C30-North Walls-Winchester Hampshire Fire Brigade
GXN207	7	TLP	43	58	Essex County	C Div-Tunbridge Wells-Kent FB-1958
GXN208	8	TL	44 ?	71	Devon	N01 Barnstaple-Devon CFB-1955 E21 Yeovil-Somerset FB-1971
GXN209	9	TL	43	67	Barry (South Wales)	B6 Barry-Glamorgan CFB-1946 C11 Tonypandy-1948 C6 Whitchurch-Cardiff City FB-1967
GXN210	10	TLP	43	71	West Sussex	Worthing Fire Station-A01 Ardsheal Rd-Worthing West Sussex FB-1971 **Preserved**
GXN211	11	TL	44 ?	73	Essex County	A2 Cowdrey Rd-Colchester-Essex CFB-1948 W1-Rhyl-Flintshire FB-Queensferry- Flintshire FB-1972ʼ Reserve-1973/**Sold to BAE Chester/Preserved**
GXN212	12	TLP	44	56	Hampshire	A1-Basingstoke-Hampshire FB-1946 B15 Gosport-Hampshire FB-1948 London Rd-High Wycombe-1956 Buckinghamshire FB
GXN213	13	TLP	44 ?	66	Isle of Wight	Cowes Fire Station-Isle of White-1945 1 Newport-Isle of White Fire Brigade-**Sold to BHC Cowes**
GXN214	14	TLP	44 ?	64	Redhill/Reigate (Surrey)	**Redhill Fire Station-?** / Chertsey Fire Station-1964 Surrey County Council Fire Brigade
GXN215	15	TL	43	71	West Sussex	Chichester Fire Station A17-Northgate-Chichester
GXN216	16	TLP	44	60	Berkshire	C4 Newbury-Reading & Berkshire FB-1948 B1 Aylesbury-Buckinghamshire FB-1956 C1-London Rd-High Wycombe-1960 Buckinghamshire FB
GXN217	17	TLP	42	60	Wiltshire	Sailsbury Fire Station-1945 Lansdowne Rd-Cheltenham-1946-Gloucestershire CFS Swindon Fire Station-1958/ 1/1 Drove Rd-Swindon-WFB
GXN218	18	TLP	42	75	Somerset	Bridgewater Fire Station-1946 Taunton Fire Station-1965
GXN219	19	TLP	44 ?	64	Merthyr Tydfil (Wales)	#1 Merthyr-Merthyr Tydfil FB-1946 A5 Port Talbot-Glamorgan CFB-1948 C1 Pontypridd-Glamorgan CFB-1964 **Parts used to restore GXN221**
GXN220	20	TLP	44 ?	?	Hertfordshire	E10 Letchworth-Hertfordshire CFB-1948 West Riding of Yorkshire FB/ **Preserved**

GXN221	21	TLP	44	63	Herefordshire	W46-St Owen St-Hereford-Herefordshire CFB **Preserved**
GXN222	22	TLP	**44 ?**	58	East Sussex	A2 Hove St-Hove-East Sussex County FB
GXN223	23	TLP	44	75	Carmarthen & Cardiganshire (Wales)	A2 Carmarthen-C&Cardiganshire FB-1948 C1 Aberystwyth-C&Cardiganshire FB-1975/**Preserved**
GXN224	24	TLP	44	74	Caernarvonshire (Wales)	A1 Bangor-Caernarvonshire FB-1968 C23 Pwhelli-Caernarvonshire FB-1974 **Preserved**
GXN225	25	TLP	44	72	Norfolk	B47 Kilhams Way- Kings Lynn-Norfolk Fire Brigade **Preserved**
GXN226	26	TLP	44	62	Durham	A1 The Sands-Durham-Durham County FB-1959 A1 Finchale Rd-Framwellgate Moor-Durham-1962
GXN227	27	TLP	**44 ?**	72	Kesteven (Lincolnshire)	Boston-1945/ **Grantham- ?**/Gainsborough Fire Station's-Kesteven CB / **Preserved**
GXN228	28	TLP	**44 ?**	66	East Riding-Humber	Stn2 Bridlington-East Riding of Yorkshire FB-1961 Stn1 Beverley-East Riding YFB -1966/**Preserved**
GXN229	29	TLP	**44 ?**	61	Glasgow (Scotland)	Glasgow Area-1945 / Ayr Fire Station
GXN230	30	TLP	44	60	Kesteven (Gainsborough)	Gainsborough-Lincolnshire-1948 Tamworth Rd-Long Eaton-1959 Elliston Rd-Glossop-1960/Derbyshire Fire Service

The National Fire Service was allocated fifty 50 foot manually operated Turntable Ladders in 1944. Many of these appliances, like GXN214 which served Surrey, were fitted with front mounted Barton pumps. This picture illustrates the wind down jacks and turning levers for extending the ladders. *Keith Wardell collection*

GXN231	31	TLP	44 ?	64	South Western (Scotland)	Dunfriese, South Western Area Fire Brigade **Preserved**
GXN232	32	TLP	44 ?	60	Perth & Kinross (Scotland)	High St-Perth -Perth & Kinross Fire Brigade
GXN233	33	TLP	44	62	Cheshire	C1 Macon Way-Crewe-Cheshire County Fire Brigade
GXN234	34	TLP	44	59	Lancashire	C54 Lacey St-Widnes-Lancashire CFB-1948 Stn1 Parade St-St Helens CBFB-1959
GXN235	35	TLP	44 ?	62	West Riding of Yorkshire (Dewsbury)	A16-Ripon-West Riding YFB-1946 B19 Selby-West Riding YFB-1951 Knottingley-West Riding YFB-1962
GXN236	36	TLP	44	71	Staffordshire	**Leek Fire Station- ?/** Stafford Fire Station-1971-Staffordshire
GXN237	37	TLP	42	54	South Yorkshire	Barnsley Fire Station-Barnsley County Borough FB
GXN238	38	TLP	44 ?	68	Edinburgh (Scotland)	**Edinburgh- ? /** Falkirk-Clydebank-Stirling Fire Stations **Preserved**
GXN239	39	TLP	44 ?	?	Durham County	C25 West Row-Stockton-Durham County -1946 D01 Ayr-South Western Area FB
GXN240	40	TLP	44 ?	57	Nottinghamshire	#1 Rosemary St-Mansfield-City of Mansfield-Nottinghamshire
GXN241	41	TLP	44 ?	?	West Riding of Yorkshire	Todmorden Fire Station-West Riding of Yorkshire FB
GXN242	42	TLP	44	63	Peterborough	Dogsthorpe Rd-Huntingdonshire & Peterborough FB-1947 Stafford-Staffordshire FB-1963
GXN243	43	TL	44	62	Derbyshire	B1 Compton Grove-Buxton-Derbyshire FB-1959 B3 Glossop-Derbyshire FB-1962
GXN244	44	TLP	44	59	Derbyshire	A2 Tamworth Rd-Long Eaton-Derbyshire FB-1948 A1 Derby Rd-Ilkeston-Derbyshire FB-1959
GXN245	45	TLP	44	62	Warwickshire	Nuneaton Fire Station-Warwick County Fire Brigade
GXN246	46	TLP	44	65	Northamptonshire (Kettering)	**Kettering Fire Station-Northampton- ?** A1 Bridge St-Loughborough / Leicestershire & Rutland FB
GXN247	47	TLP	44 ?	67	Northern Area Fire Brigade (Scotland)	Inverness Fire Station-1967 Northern Area Fire Brigade
GXN248	48	TLP	45	60	Liverpool	Mill Lane-Wallasey County Borough/ **Period at Congleton- ?**
GXN249	49	TLP	44 ?	?	Glasgow	Fire Station Unknown
GXN250	50	TLP	45	65	Norfolk	Friars Lane-Great Yarmouth County Borough FB **Scrapped 1975**

					Austin FG & FJ & LD Weight LD/1-1.5 Tons FG/1.5-5 Tons FJ/up to 18 Tons	**Austin Motors became part of BMC (British Motor Corporation) in 1952 when it merged with Morris Motors. Austin K2 & K4 will be found under a seperate listing. For full details of different types of Austin chassis see BMC listing.**
WG1936		ET	38	?	Central Area Fire Brigade (Scotland)	Falkirk Fire Station Limousine-
FUD987		Lighting Unit	52	?	Oxfordshire Fire Service	C01 The Broadway-Didcot A40-OFB
PED555		Res/T	55	69	Warrington County Borough Fire Brigade	Heathside-Warrington-1968/Winwick St-Warrington-1969 FFG-Marsden
GUD901		WRC	53	74	Oxfordshire Fire Service	**ex County Council /** Kidlington Fire Station-**Dark Green** NC Loadstar-
OPA879		CAV	53	64	Surrey County Council Fire Brigade	173 Cobham Rd-Leatherhead K8 Wayfarer-
818FPJ		F/Salv	54	74	Surrey County Council Fire Brigade	Reigate Fire Station 503-
8059PO		ET MW/Shop	54	74	West Sussex Fire Brigade	West Mead's Drive-Bognor Regis LD 30cwt
VNB243		C/Unit	58	74	City of Manchester	E50 London Rd-Manchester 152-Lomas

The Austin FFG chassis was used by the Cornwall County Fire Brigade for two Water Carriers and 233NAF, a Foam Tender. The back of the appliance had large fold-back doors which exposed the working part of the appliance. The machine was originally delivered as a Hose & Pump Carrier and looked really strange. *Michael Lawmon*

| 999GNU | | F/Salv | 58 | 82 | Derbyshire Fire Service | B1 Crompton Grove-Buxton 503-Reeves Burgess |
| 999JRA | | F/Salv | 59 | 82 | Derbyshire Fire Service | C1 Sheffield Rd-Chesterfield |

999JRB		F/Salv	59	82	Derbyshire Fire Service	503-Reeves Burgess A2 Tamworth Rd-Long Eaton-1974 D2 Nottingham Rd-Derby-1982 503-Reeves Burgess

80 JPE is an Austin FFK fitted with HCB bodywork as a foam salvage tender, and was used in that form by Surrey Fire Service. *The Wardell Collection*

OHR514		ET SalvT	59	?	Wiltshire Fire Brigade	**ex Mobile Workshop** Drove Rd-Swindon NC Loadstar-WFB
80JPE		F/Salv	59	74	Surrey County Council Fire Brigade	29 Church St-Woking 503-HCB
79GPK		F/Salv	59	74	Surrey County Council Fire Brigade	Epsom Fire Station 503-HCB
7351VX		BAT	60	72	Essex County Fire Brigade	C51 North Rd-Brentwood LD-
RHS520		H/FoT	60	?	Western Area Fire Brigade Scotland)	Canal St-Paisley FFG-HCB
233NAF		FOT	61	?	Cornwall County Fire Brigade	**ex Hose & Pump Carrier - ?** / A4 College St-Camborne Drake-
974ORL		WRC	61	72	Cornwall County Fire Brigade	A4 College St-Camborne Drake-
87RAF		WRC	62	72	Cornwall County Fire Brigade	A1 St Georges Rd-Truro-1970 /A1 Station Rd-Truro-1972 Drake-
JJK200		ET	62	67	Eastbourne County Borough Fire Brigade	Whitley Rd-Eastbourne LD-ECBFB
UHS171		H/Fot	62	?	Western Area Fire Brigade (Scotland)	Rue End St-Greenock FFG/HCB
VDO600		E/Salv/T	63	?	Holland County Fire Brigade	**Converted to Road Accident Vehicle** FFG-Carmichael
XDO545		Pump/RT Salv/T		?	Holland County Fire Brigade	**Converted to Road Accident Vehicle** FGK-Carmichael
ACC537B		Res/T	63	74	Caernarvonshire County FB (Wales)	Beach Rd-Bangor Mastiff-
BGG994B		C/Unit	64	?	Glasgow Fire Service (Scotland)	C4 Kelvinhaugh St-West Marine FFG-Bennett-Mitchell
DGA918B		CAV	64	?	Glasgow Fire Service (Scotland)	A1 Ingram St-Central/ C4 Kelvinhaugh St-West Marine LD5-Bennett-Mitchell
BKD701B		FOT	64	?	City of Liverpool	#15 Banks Rd-Speke Airport LD 30cwt
EHH163C		ET	64	**68?**	City of Carlisle	Warwick Street-Carlisle-**Used as an Emergency Tender** A35-CoCFB
JKD121D		Artic/TU	66	81	City of Liverpool	#1 Hatton Gardens-Liverpool-1969 #1 Studholme St-Bankhall-1974 C1 Studholme St-Bankhall-1981 Merseyside Fire Brigade /**Articulated Unit** FFK240-Tasker
ESA597D		CAV	66	?	North Eastern Area Fire Brigade (Scotland)	North Anderson Drive-Aberdeen FFG-Federal Industries
NKD162F		Artic/TU	67	81	City of Liverpool	#1 Hatton Gardens-Liverpool-1969 #1 Studholme St-Bankhall-1974 C1 Studholme St-Bankhall-1981 Merseyside Fire Brigade /**Articulated Unit** Austin FJK240
NLV956F		Hi-ex FoT	67	70	City of Liverpool	#8 Mather Ave-Liverpool-1968 #1 Hatton Gardens-Liverpool-1970 30cwt-
NGE656F		Hi-ex Fot	68	85	Glasgow Fire Service (Scotland)	#1 Ingram St-Central-1975 A01 Ingram St-Central-1985 /Strathclyde Fire Brigade FFG-Bennett

					Austin K2 Chassied Specialist Appliances		The Austin K2 was a 2-3 ton chassis cab which was supplied in large numbers during the Second World War for towing duties. It was used for a variety of other uses at the end of war, and many were used well into the 1960's. They were powered by 6 cylinder petrol engines.
GGX285		P/SalvT	41	?	Kent Fire Brigade		Gillingham
GGX448		Control Unit	41	63	City of Liverpool		Hatton Gardens
GGX481		Foam Carrier	41	54	Middlesbrough Fire Brigade		Middlesbrough
GGX576		ET/SalvT	41	?	Fife Fire Brigade (Scotland)		Methil
GGX765		Canteen	41	?	Essex County Fire Brigade		
GGN626		ET	41	?	Hereford County Fire Brigade		Hereford
GLC708		Foam /T	41	66	Norfolk Fire Brigade		Kings Lynn
GLC751		ET	41	66	Cornwall County Fire Brigade		Camborne/**Transfered to Devon County**
GLC765		CAV	41	?	West Riding of Yorkshire		Shipley
GLC780		Salv/T	41	?	City of Bristol		
GLC827		MobileW	41	?	Durham County Fire Brigade		Framwellgate
GLC875		Salv/T	41	53	Lancashire County Fire Brigade		Ashton under Lyne
GLE32		Salv/T	41	?	South Eastern Area Fire Brigade (Scotland)		Leith
GLE82		ET	41	?	City of Manchester		
GLE313		ET	41	68	Devon County Fire Brigade		Barnstaple-1955 Exmouth-1965
GLE545		ET	41	55	Bootle Fire Brigade		Bootle
GLE630		P/SalvT	41	52	Kent Fire Brigade		Dover

999JRA was an unusual-looking Austin 503 chassied Foam and Salvage Tender, that had bodywork by Reeves Burgess. Three were delivered to the Derbyshire Fire Service between 1958 and 1959, the others also carry distinctive registration numbers of 999GNU for Buxton and 999JRB which went to Long Eaton. The example illustrated served at Chesterfield.
Ron Henderson

GLE821		Salvage Tender	41	?	City of Manchester	Miles Platting
GLE900		Foam/C	41	54	City of Bristol	Avonmouth
GLE980		Foam/T	41	58	North Riding of Yorkshire	Grangemouth
GJJ338		ET	42	67	West Hartlepool Fire Brigade	West Hartlepool
GJJ345		Foam/T	42	54	City of Kingston upon Hull Fire Brigade	Hull Central
GLR244		Salvage Tender	42	60	City of Kingston upon Hull Fire Brigade	Hull East
GLR319		Pump Salvage	42	?	Kent Fire Brigade	West Wickham
GLR516		Pump Salvage	42	52	Kent Fire Brigade	Folkestone
GLR553		ET	42	72	Caernarvonshire Fire Brigade (Wales)	Holyhead
GLR581		Salvage Tender	42	60	City of Kingston upon Hull Fire Brigade	Hull West
GLR857		Pump Salvage	42	?	Kent Fire Brigade	Ashford
GLR869		Foam/T	42	?	City of Portsmouth	Corsham
GLR910		ET	42	62	City of York	York
GLR988		ET	42	?	Central Area Fire Brigade (Scotland)	Falkirk
GLT247		Pump Salvage	42	?	Kent Fire Brigade	Hythe
GLT260		ET	42	66	City of Cardiff	Cardiff
GLT265		ET	42	60	South Shields County Borough	Kepple St-South Shields
GLT270		Canteen	42	?	Durham County Fire Brigade	Framwellgate
GLT427		Salvage Tender	42	?	Lancashire County Fire Brigade	Stretford
GLT494		Pump Salvage	42	?	Kent Fire Brigade	Chatham
GLT588		BApp/t	42	?	West Riding of Yorkshire	Cleckheaton
GLT615		Pump Salvage	42	?	Devon County Fire Brigade	Camels Head
GLT631		Canteen	42	?	Cornwall County Fire Brigade	
GLT684		ET	42	?	Central Area Fire Brigade (Scotland)	Clydebank
GLT941		Control Unit	42	56	Kent Fire Brigade	Maidstone
GUU51		ET	42	61	City of Liverpool	Hatton Gardens
GXM175		Control Unit	43	72?	Durham County Fire Brigade	Framwellgate-**Long wheelbase Version**
GXH39		Salvage Tender	43	62	City of York	York
GXH45		Salvage Tender	43	59	City of Kingston upon Hull Fire Brigade	Hull Central
GXH190		Pump Salvage	43	52	Kent Fire Brigade	Margate
GXH281		Pump Salvage	43	?	Buckinghamshire Fire Brigade	Aylesbury
GXH303		Salvage Tender	43	?	East Sussex Fire Brigade	Halton
GXH328		Pump Salvage	43	?	Kent Fire Brigade	Maidstone
GXH335		Canteen	43	?	Glamorgan County Fire Brigade	

GXH338		Foam/T	43	72	Dorset Fire Brigade	Poole
GXH355		Canteen Van	43	?	Glamorgan County Fire Brigade (Wales)	Bridgend
GXH392		Pump Salvage	43	52	Kent Fire Brigade	Royal Tunbridge Wells
GXH536		Pump Salvage	43	52	Kent Fire Brigade	Canterbury
GXH546		Canteen Van	43	61	City of Liverpool	Hatton Gardens
GXH600		Foam Carrier	43	75?	Glasgow Fire Service	Ardrossan
GXH626		Canteen	43	73	Cheshire Fire Brigade	Northwich
GXH677		Canteen Van	43	?	Middlesex Fire Brigade	Edmonton
GXH701		Foam/T	43	60	Sunderland Fire Brigade	Dun Cow St-Sunderland
GXH729		ET	43	53	Middlesbrough Fire Brigade	Middlesbrough
GXH787		ET	43	65	Glamorgan County Fire Brigade (Wales)	Pontypridd
GXH815		Control Unit	43	?	West Riding of Yorkshire	Elland
GXH945		Pump Salvage	43	?	Kent Fire Brigade	Bromley
GXH970		Salvage Tender	43	66	Norfolk Fire Brigade	Kings Lynn
GXH983		Foam/T	43	?	Caernarvonshire Fire Brigade (Wales)	Bangor
GXH985		Pump Salvage	43	?	Kent Fire Brigade	Rochester
GXA732		Foam/T	**43**	?	Pembrokeshire Fire Brigade (Wales)	Haverfordwest

Wartime GXM175 which is based in an Austin K2 chassis was one of many that went from fighting fires as a pumping appliance, to fighting fires in a specialist role. This version was rare in that it had a longer wheelbase as can be seen in this photograph. The bodywork was provided by Durham County Fire Brigade, who had an excellent reputation for thier body building. This 1940s pump later became a Control Unit which served into the 1970s. *Ian Moore*

BEDFORD

Reg No	Fleet No	TYPE	YR	OS	Appliance & Brigade Name	Details/Stations
					Bedford SL & SH & TKL & TL Magirus Turntable Ladders	
VTJ416		TL	55	66	Lancashire County Fire Brigade	8.1 Windermere Rd-Leigh-1966/Reserve-1967 **Sold Isle of White FB-Newport-1967** SL-Morris-Magirus-100'L
100ABH		TL	56	71	Buckinghamshire Fire Brigade	1 Cambridge St- Aylesbury SH-Haydon-Magirus-100'L
PVP665	19	TL	56	68	City of Birmingham	A2 Ettington Rd-Aston-Birmingham SH-Morris-Magirus-100'L
886BKO	199	TL	58	80	Kent Fire Brigade	D Div Old Dover Rd-Canterbury SH-Morris-Magirus-100'L
887BKO	200	TL	58	80	Kent Fire Brigade	B Div Watling St-Medway SH-Morris-Magirus-100'L
546DKN	187	TL	58	82?	Kent Fire Brigade	A Div Park Farm Drive-Folkestone SH-Morris-Magirus-100'L
547DKN	188	TL	58	82?	Kent Fire Brigade	C Div Grove Hill Rd-Royal Tunbridge Wells SH-Morris-Magirus-100'L
481HKE	186	TL	59	80?	Kent Fire Brigade	D Div King St-Margate **Sold to Wren Davis Ltd in Buckinghamshire** SH-Morris-Magirus-100'L
WWV439		TL	60	80	Wiltshire Fire Brigade	1/1 Drove Rd-Swindon-Wiltshire S-Haydon-Magirus-100'L **Preserved**

Pictured at High Wycombe in Buckinghamshire is Bedford SH which was fitted with a Haydon-Magirus Turntable Ladder. 100ABH was new in 1956 and served most of its time at Aylesbury. This illustrates the earlier type of Magirus Ladder, which had a turret that was open to the elements; later models being enclosed. This machine is fitted with large chrome bumpers that were a feature of the time on many vehicle types.
Keith Wardell collection

Reg	No	Type		Year	Brigade	Details
EM7377		TL	60	79	Bootle Fire Brigade	Strand Rd-Bootle-Liverpool-1974 C6 Strand Rd-Bootle-1979 /Merseyside FB SL-Haydon-Magirus-100'L
375EOX	22	TL	61	76	City of Birmingham	Lancaster Circus-1 Central-1974 A1 Lancaster Circus-Central-1976 West Midlands FS TK-Haydon-Magirus-100'L
376EOX	8	TL	61	78	City of Birmingham	5 Moseley Rd-1970 /5 Bristol Rd-Bournbrook-1974 C4 Bristol Rd-Bournbrook-1978 /West Midlands FS **Sold to Kent Fire Brigade-1980** TK-Haydon-Magirus-100'L
UMS197		TL	62	80	Central Area Fire Brigade (Scotland)	Clydebank-Central Area FB-1974 F01 Clydebank-Strathclyde FB-1978 **L Re-ch onto S& Drewry WY-XGG731S-Strathclyde FB** TK-Haydon-Magirus-100'L
WCX744		TL	62	83	Huddersfield County Borough FB	Outcote Bank-1974 C11 Outcote Bank Huddersfield-1983 West Yorkshire FS TK-Haydon-Magirus-100'L
ERP978C		TL	65	86	Northamptonshire Fire Brigade	A1 The Headlands-Kettering Northamptonshire KGL-Haydon-Magirus-100'L
CFC601Y		TL	82		Oxfordshire Fire Service	B01 Rewley Rd-Oxford TL1630-Carmichael-Magirus DL30U
YIA5121		TL	85		Northern Ireland Fire Brigade	A05 Springfield Rd-Springfield-Belfast TL1630-Carmichael-Magirus DL30U
C808OVV		TL	86	94	Northamptonshire Fire Brigade	The Headlands-Kettering/**Written off in RTA** TL1630-Carmichael-Magirus DL30U

	MW-No				**Bedford SL & TKGL Merryweather Turntable Ladders**	**Merryweather Ladder No**
6PTB	655 MW-26	TL	60	73	Lancashire County Fire Brigade	6.1 Ellen St-Nelson-1966/5.1 Manchester Rd-Accrington-1973 SL-Merryweather-100'L
7PTB	656 MW-27	TL	60	72?	Lancashire County Fire Brigade	2.1 Clarke St-Morecambe **Underwent loan period in Fife, Scotland.** SL-Merryweather-100'L
8PTB	657 MW-38	TL	60	76	Lancashire County Fire Brigade	11.6 Park Rd-Stretford-Lancashire CFB-1967 Training Centre-1974 **Transferred to Greater Manchester FS-1976** SL-Merryweather-100'L
9PTB	658 MW-39	TL	60	72	Lancashire County Fire Brigade	10.1 Wellington Rd-Ashton under Lyne-1967/Reserve-1972 SL-Merryweather-100'L
769FMJ	MW-52	TLP	63	79	Bedfordshire Fire Brigade	01 Barkers Lane-Bedford-1979 **Ladders Re-chassied ERF84PS G&T Power CNM455T** TKGL-Merryweather-100'L
232JBM	MW-62	TLP	63	71	Bedfordshire Fire Service	Studley Rd-Luton-1965-Studley Rd-Luton-Luton CB **Sold to Greene King Brewery FB-Bury St Edmonds-1988** **Preserved** TKGL-Merryweather-100'L
435DVJ	MW-66	TLP	63	92	Hereford County Fire Brigade	Owen St-Hereford-1974 /46 Owen St-Hereford-1992 Hereford & Worcester /**Preserved by staff at Bromsgrove FS** TKGL-Merryweather-100'L
RFA868	301 MW-63	TLP	63	85	Burton upon Trent County BFB	High St-Burton upon Trent-1974 ND Burton upon Trent-1985 Staffordshire FB **Preserved by staff at Burton upon Trent FS** TKGL-Merryweather-100'L
405JFR	251 MW-85	TLP	64	79	Blackpool County Borough FB	B30 Albert Rd-Blackpool-1974 A37 St Annes Rd-South Shore-Blackpool-1977-Lancashire FB A31 Redbank Rd-Bispham-Blackpool-LCFB-1979/**Preserved** TKGL-Merryweather-100'L

ERP978C fetures a Magirus 100' Turntable Ladder with an enclosed turret and mounted on the Bedford KGL chassis. This vehicle entered service in 1965 and incorporates the folding type of crew doors that were then gaining popularity. Based at Kettering, the machine was replaced by another Bedford with Magirus ladder's in 1986 in its 21 years service though the replacement was, unfortunately, written off in an accident in 1994. *Les Edkins*

CTA298C	ER-3	TLP	65	83	Devon County Fire Brigade	N02 Marlborough Rd-Ilfracombe **Ladders off Austin K4 GXN203-Preserved** TK-Merryweather-60'L
VTB321D	885 MW-111	TLP	66	82	Lancashire County Fire Brigade	6.1 Ellen St-Nelson-1974/E09 Belvidere Rd-Burnley-1982 TK-Merryweather-100'L
VTB322D	886 MW-112	TLP	66	80	Lancashire County Fire Brigade	8.1 Windermere Rd-Leigh-1974 B27 Windermere Rd-Leigh -1980 Greater Manchester FS TK-Merryweather-100'L
BTB291E	949 MW-121	TLP	67	75	Lancashire County Fire Brigade	10.1 Wellington St-Ashton under Lyne-1971 E73 Hodgeson St-Ashton under Lyne- Reserve-1975 Greater Manchester FS TK-Merryweather- 100'L
BTB292E	950 MW-122	TLP	67	83	Lancashire County Fire Brigade	11.1 Park Rd-Stretford-1972/2.1 Clarke St-Morecambe-1983 TK-Merryweather-100'L
HCD999E	32 MW-130	TLP	67	84	Brighton County Borough FB	Preston Circus-Brighton-1974 A04 Preston Circus-Brighton-1984 East Sussex FB/**Preserved** TKGL-Merryweather-100'L
WMB700E	MW-131	TLP	67	85	Cheshire County Fire Brigade	C8 Chester Rd-Lymm-Cheshire-1981 B1 Winwick St-Warrington-1981 Reserve- 1985 TKGL-Merryweather-100'L

					Bedford TKEL & KM Hydraulic Platforms	
531VU		HP	63	75	City of Manchester	London Rd-City of Manchester-1974 E50 London Rd-Greater Manchester CFS-1975 **Fitted with a Leyland Engine** TKEL-Cocker-Simon SS65
164YFK		PHP	64	82	Worcester City & County FB	Castle Rd-Kidderminster-Worcester City &CFB-1974 24 Castle Rd- Kidderminster-Hereford &Worcester FB **Sold National Exhibition Centre-Birmingham** TKEL-Angus Fire Fly-Simon **DS50**

164YFK, a small Bedford TKEL with Angus Fire Fly bodywork is seen here equipped with Simon DS50 hydraulic booms. It was delivered to the Kidderminster station of the Worcester City & CFB in 1964 and went on to serve for 16 years after which it was sold to the then newly opened National Exhibition Centre in Birmingham. Other sets of DS50 booms were found on a Leyland Comet at Burnley and an Albion at Halifax.
Michael Lawmon

DYB107C		HP	65	82	Somerset Fire Brigade	Salmon Parade-Bridgewater-1982 TKEL-HCB-Angus-Simon-SS65
BEX812C		HP	65	82	Great Yarmouth County FB	Friars Lane-Great Yarmouth CFB-1974 C69 Friars Lane-Great Yarmouth Norfolk FB TKEL-HCB-Angus-Simon- SS65
MSG31F		HP	67	86	South Eastern Area Fire Brigade (Scotland)	Marrionville Fire Station - Sight Hill Fire Station Lothian &Borders FB/Reserve- 1986 TKEL-SMT-Simon-SS65-
JEF254G	37 3	PHP	68	84	West Hartlepool Fire Brigade	Stranton-West Hartlepool CFB-1974 9 Stranton-West Hartlepool-1984/Cleveland CFB TKEL Angus Simon SS50
KKY999G		HP	68	84	City of Bradford	Nelson St-City of Bradford FB-1974 A11 Nelson St-Bradford- 1980 / **Named 'Henry Sissling'** West Yorkshire FS/Training School- 1984 KM-Carmichael-Wibbe-Orbitor 72'
GJK600H		PHP	70	88	Eastbourne County Borough FB	Bourne St-Eastbourne CBFB-1974 B11 Bourne St-Eastbourne-1988 /East Sussex FB TKEL-HCB Angus-Simon-SS50
NFG249H		PHP	70	93	Fife Fire Brigade (Scotland)	A3 Dunnikeir Rd-Kirkaldy-1981 / Glenrothes Headquarters (Reserve) - TKEL-HCB-Angus-Simon SS50
FFO606K	13-5	HP	72	95	Brecon & Radnor Joint Fire Brigade (Wales)	Tremont Rd- Llandrindod Wells-1974 S13 Tremont Rd-Llandrindod Wells-1995-Powys Fire Service **Sold to BAA Heathrow Airport London** TK- HCB Angus-Simon SS70

Seen here is 1960 Bedford S/Haydon bodied Turntable Ladder WWV439, a specific model built for Wiltshire Fire Brigade. The Magirus ladders on this appliance served Swindon for over twenty years. Wiltshire mounted large wooden plaques of the county crest on the doors as can be seen in this photograph. Also popular at the time was the roof skylight.
Michael Lawmon

					Bedford WLD & TJ4L & SB & RL Emergency/Rescue Tenders	
CTN292		ET	35	?	Newcastle Fire Brigade	Pilgrim St-Newcastle WLD-N&GFB
GR5951	No 5	ET	38	60	Sunderland Fire Brigade	Dun Cow St-Sunderland-1960 WLD-White
FYH83		ET	40	65	Blackburn County Borough Fire Brigade	ex Heavy Pump/Byrom Rd-Blackburn K-BCBFB
GZ19		ET	44	55	Belfast Fire Brigade (Northern Ireland)	Central Fire Station-Belfast-1954 OB-Home Office
FA6946		ET	?	66	Burton upon Trent County Borough	High Street- Burton upon Trent K-BuTCB
DBM789		ET	51	65	Luton County Borough Fire Brigade	Studley Rd-Luton K-Superline Bodies
LOY999	11ET	ET	53	74	Croydon County Borough FB	Old Town-Croydon-1965/H31 Croydon-1972/Reserve-1974 S-Carmichael
CCM266	7 1002	ET	53	? 75	Birkenhead County Borough FB	Whetstone Lane-Charring Cross-Birkenhead- ? / Merseyside S-HCB
LYO805		ET	53	75	Great Yarmouth County Borough Fire Brigade	Friars Lane-Great Yarmouth- ? / Norfolk FB SP-HOS
KRN749	253	P/ET	53	74	Preston County Borough FB	Tithbarn St-Preston-1962 Blackpool Rd-Preston-1974/Short Wheelbase TJ4L-Miles
BJC666		Res/T	54	63	Caernarvonshire Fire Brigade (Wales)	Union Rd-Bangor-ex Ambulance J1-Lomas
NYV73		RAV	54	?	Tynemouth County Borough Fire Brigade	ex AFS P-1968/Preston Rd-North-Tynemouth - ? / T&WFB SP-HOS
LET397		ET	54	74	Rotherham County Borough FB	#1 Erskine Rd-Rotherham-1972 #2 Oaks Lane-Rotherham-1974/Res-South Yorkshire-1976 SB-Wilsdon-Yellow livery
KKW600		E/ST CU	54	78	City of Bradford	Nelson St-Bradford-1974/ Named ' W Marshall Hind ' A11 Bradford-West Yorkshire FS-1978 S-HCB
MDK234		ET	56	72	Rochdale County Borough FB	MacClure Rd-Rochdale-1972 S-HCB
OCY22		ET	56	74	City of Swansea (Wales)	Grove Place-Swansea-1974 / 5 Swansea-West Glamorgan S-Miles
943ANK		ET	57	80	Hertfordshire County Council FB	St Albans Rd-Garston-1974/Converted Control Unit-1980 TJ4L-Miles
TCR644	No-8	ET	57	75	City of Southampton	St Mary's Rd-St Marys-Southampton-1974 D54 St Mary's-Hampshire FS SP-HCB
KCH999		ET	57	76	Derby County Borough Fire Brigade	Nottingham Rd-Derby- 1974-Converted Foam Salv/T D2 Nottingham Rd-Derbyshire FS-1976 TJ4L-Miles
SFR873		P/ET	58	72	Blackpool County Borough FB	Albert Rd-Blackpool-1972 S-HCB
52HNK		ET	59	74	Hertfordshire County Council FB	Letchworth Fire Station-1967/St Georges Way-Stevenage-1974 TJ4L-Miles
TBU999		Pump E/ST	59	76	Oldham County Borough FB	Ascroft St-Oldham-1974 C33 Oldham-Greater Manchester FS-1971 Converted Salvage Tender A10 The Crescent-Salford-Greater Manchester-1976 TJ4L-Miles
NHL190		E/ST	59	78	City of Wakefield	Brunswick St-Wakefield-1974 F11 Wakefield-West Yorkshire FS-1978 TJ4L-HCB
PBR500	No-7	ET	60	72	Sunderland Fire Brigade	#1 Dun Cow St-Sunderland TJ4L-Miles

VDN100	No-6	ET	60	79	City of York	Clifford St-York-1974 SD1 Clifford St York-North Yorkshire FB-1979 **4x4 WD** RL-Derwent-**Yellow livery**
RHM110	10ET ST8	ET	60	71	East Ham County Borough FB	High St East Ham-1965 /F21 East Ham-1971 **Converted Salvage Tender** /G30 Harrow Rd-Wembley-1976 S-Miles
344GPT	220	ET	60	74	Durham County Fire Brigade	Hedgley Rd-Hebburn-1965 B16 Victoria Rd-Hebburn-1974/Tyne & Wear MFB TJ4L-Miles
152DUP	221	ET	60	86	Durham County Fire Brigade	Belasis Rd-Billingham-1965 / S1 Darlington-1977 **Converted Breathing Apparatus Tender** N1 Finchale Rd-Durham-1986 TJ4L-Miles
GEO224		ET	60	76	Barrow in Furrness County Brigade FB	Abbey Rd-Barrow-1974/BD Abbey Rd-Barrow-Cumbria FS TJ4L-Miles
115CER		ET	60	80	Cambridgeshire Fire & Rescue Service	Parkside-Cambridge-1980/**4x4 WD** RLHZ-Papworth Industries
TVH259		ET	61	79	Huddersfield County Borough FB	Outcote Bank-Huddersfield-1974 C11 Huddersfield-West Yorkshire FS TJ4L-Miles
6249PT	092	RAV	61	?	Durham County Fire Brigade	**ex WRT-Durham-1970**/A12 Edward Rd-Birtley-1974 D19 Central Ave-Newton Aycliffe-1976 TJ5-HCB/DCFB
6245PT	094	RAV	61	?	Durham County Fire Brigade	**ex WRT-Durham-1969**/B11 Woodstone-Fencehouses-1970 TJ5-HCB-DCFB

Bedford K DBM789 is a Pump/ Emergency Tender which served for almost 15 years at Studley Road in Luton. It was replaced in 1965 by another Bedford, a TKEL with Dennis/ Miles bodywork. Just visible in the photograph is the hose reel and a large oxygen acetylene cylinder used for cutting metal at special service calls.
Keith Wardell collection

XUF999	22	ET	62	85	Brighton County Borough FB	4 Preston Circus-Brighton-1974 A4 Preston Circus-Brighton-1980 / **Converted BApp/T-1985** East Sussex FB/**Preserved** TJ4L-Miles
LEF927	4	ET	62	78	County Borough of Hartlepool FB	Stranton-West Hartlepool-1974 9 Stranton-West Hartlepool-Cleveland CFB TJ4L-Miles
6091DF		Res/T	63	75	Gloucestershire Fire Service	12 Keynsham Rd-Cheltenham-1975/**4x4 WD** RLHZ-Bates Holmes Crane
BBE157B		ET	64	83	Lindsey County FB (Lincolnshire)	Laneham St-Scunthorpe-1974 / D1 Scunthorpe-Humberside FB SB-HCB Angus
AEH513C		ET	65	81	City of Stoke on Trent Fire Brigade	Bethesda St-Hanley-Stoke-1974 ND Bethesda St-Hanley-Staffordshire FB-1981 /**4x4 WD** RL-HCB Angus
NRL384F		ET	67	82	Cornwall County Fire Brigade	B1 Launceston Rd-Bodmin-1969 B1 Berrycombe Rd-Bodmin-1982 TJ4L-HCB Angus
NRL385F		ET	67	84	Cornwall County Fire Brigade	A2 North Parade-Falmouth-1975 A2 Trescobeas Rd-Falmouth-1984-**Conv Foam Tender-1984** TJ4L-HCB Angus
LUN221F		ET	67	84	Denbighshire & Montgomeryshire FB (Wales)	Bradley Rd-Wrexham-1974 /E1 Wrexham-1984-Clwyd FS TJ4L-HCB Angus
HCB999F		ET	67	**76?**	Blackburn County Borough FB	D71/B71 Byrom Rd-Blackburn TJ-Hawson
ORL365G		ET	68	84	Cornwall County Fire Brigade	A4 College St-Cambourne-1984-**Conv Fire Prevention-1988** TJ4L-HCB Angus
PCA889H		ET	70	86	Denbighshire & Montgomeryshire FB (Wales)	Rd-Colwyn Bay-1974 W2 Colwyn Bay-1986-Clwyd FS TJ4L-Carmichael
UFW460J		ET	70	89	Lindsey County FB (Lincolnshire)	Pelham Rd-Immingham-1974 C4-Pelham Rd-Immingham-Humberside Fire Brigade SB-HCB Angus

VDN100 was photographed in 1974 shortly after City of York had become part of North Yorkshire Fire Brigade. This unusual Bedford RL Emergency Tender with Derwent bodywork was delivered to the Clifford Road station in York in 1960 in a striking yellow livery which was a feature of this brigade for many years. *Keith Wardell collection*

					Bedford TKEL & KEL & TKG & KG & TL Emergency/Rescue Tenders	
190LHY	2001	ET	61	76	City of Bristol	#1 Bridewell St-Bristol Central-1973 #1 Temple Back-Bristol-1974 A1 Temple-Bristol-County of Avon TKEL-HCB
SVL157		ET	61	82	City of Lincoln Fire Brigade	South Park Ave-Lincoln-1974 A01 Lincoln-Lincolnshire FB-1982 **Converted Fire Prevention Unit** TKEL-HCB
UMS198		ET	62	78	Central Area Fire Brigade (Scotland)	Kilbowie Rd-Clydebank-1975 F11 Clydebank-Strathclyde FB- **Written off in RTA** TKEL-Metro Cammell
JEK999	4	ET Salv/T	62	75	Wigan County Borough Fire Brigade	Chapel Lane-Wigan-1963/Robin Park Rd-Wigan-1974 B24 Wigan-1975/Greater Manchester CFS TKEL-HCB Angus
PEN999		ET Salv/T	62	74	Bury County Borough Fire Brigade	The Rock-Bury-1974 TKEL-Carmichael
1393TF	790	ET	62	72	Lancashire County Fire Brigade	E70 The Broadway-Chadderton-1972 TKEL-Carmichael
551VKX		ET	62	79	Buckinghamshire Fire Brigade	21 Tuns Lane-Slough-1974 ED 17 Tuns Lane-Slough-1979/Royal Berkshire FB TKEL-HCB
552VKX		ET	62	89	Buckinghamshire Fire Brigade	24 St Marys St-High Wycombe-1974/C1 High Wycombe-1977 **Converted Control Unit-1982/Conv Canteen Van-1989** TKEL-HCB
553VKX		ET	62	77	Buckinghamshire Fire Brigade	1 Cambridge St-Aylesbury-1974 B1 Cambridge St-Aylesbury-1977 TKEL-HCB

Bedford RLHZ 6091DF was the first of several Heavy Wreckers for Gloucestershire Fire Service. This example, which is fitted with a Bates Holmes crane, served out of Keynsham Road fire station in Cheltenham. Later cranes were mounted on AEC and Ford chassis. Of interest is the large winch on the front and the position of the bell. This machine had the added advantage of being of four wheel drive configuration.
Keith Wardell collection

Pump Salvage Tender OCP641 was photographed outside the then Halifax County fire station in Gibbert Street in the early 1960s. It had a relatively short life, serving only ten years. Unusually, the pump controls were located on the side of this appliance. Halifax County Borough had a scheme to name appliances after famous local dignitaries; this one being named 'Winifred Oxley'.
Ian Moore

UFW460G is a 1970 vintage Emergency Tender based on a Bedford SB unit. This HCB Angus-bodied appliance was another long serving machine, providing Immingham with cover for nearly two decades. Originally delivered to Lindsey County along with a sister machine at Scunthorpe, they both passed to the new Humberside Fire Brigade in 1974. *Steve Shaw*

576YTD	773	ET	62	77	Lancashire County Fire Brigade	C54 Lacey S-Widnes-1974 B5 Lacey St-Widnes-Cheshire FB-1977 KEL-Cocker
577YTD	774	ET	62	77	Lancashire County Fire Brigade	F80 Manchester Rd-Accrington-1974 D70 Manchester Rd-Accrington-1977 KEL-Cocker
578YTD	775	ET	62	77	Lancashire County Fire Brigade	B34 Weldbank Rd-Chorley-1974/E94 Bradley Rd-Nelson-1977 KEL-Cocker
928LBJ		ET	62	84	Suffolk & Ipswich Fire Brigade	Colchester Rd-Ipswich-1974 A01 Colchester Rd-1984/Ipswich-Suffolk CFS TKEL-HCB
UCL999		ET	63	81	City of Norwich	Bethel St-Norwich-1974 AD Bethel St-Norwich-Norfolk FS-1981 TKEL-HCB
YJY999		ET	63	81	City of Plymouth	Greenbank Rd-Greenbank-Plymouth-1974 W50 Greenbank-Devon FB-1981 TKEL-Mumford
445DHR		ET	63	82	Wiltshire Fire Brigade	1/1 Drove Rd-Swindon-1973 **Converted Control Unit Canteen Van** 2/1 Dallas Rd-Chippenham-1982 TKEL-Mumford
916DFH	No-5	ET	64	75	City of Gloucester	Eastern Ave-Gloucester-1974 05 Eastern Ave-Gloucester-1975/Gloucestershire FS TKEL-Dennis M
311LEW		ET	64	82	Huntingdonshire & Peterborough FB	6 Hartford Rd-Huntingdon-1974 /N27 Huntingdon-1982 N20 Horsefair-Wisbech-Cambridgeshire F&RS-1985 Cambridgeshire Fire & Rescue Service TKEL-HCB
FMA292B		ET	64	83	Cheshire County Fire Brigade	D8 Dock Rd South-Bebbington-1974 W2 Bebbington-Merseyside MFB-1983 TKEL-HCB Angus
AMB586B		ET	64	77	Cheshire County Fire Brigade	A1 Railway St-Hyde-1974 E57 Hyde-1977/Greater Manchester County FS TKEL-HCB Angus
AFJ333B		ET	64	80	City of Exeter	#1 Howell Rd-Exeter-1974/E32 Exeter-Devon FB-1980 TKEL-Mumford
BWM602B		ET	64	78	Southport County Borough Fire Brigade	Manchester Rd-Southport-1974 N7 Southport-Merseyside MFB-1978 TKEL-Carmichael
DTD808B	807	ET	64	77	Lancashire County Fire Brigade	2.2 Quarry Rd-Lancaster-1973/2.2 Cable St-Lancaster-1974 A11 Lancaster-1978 TKEL-Busmar
EUE104C		ET/CU	65	85	Warwick County Fire Brigade	41 Leamington -Royal Leamington Spa-1974 SD 29 Leamington-1977/SD 29-**Control Unit**-1985 TKEL-HCB
DXC991C		ET	65	79	Solihull County Borough FB	Streetsbrook Rd-Solihull-1974 /B1 Solihull-1976 C8 Brook Lane-Billesley-1977 B7 Northway-NEC-Bickenhill-1979 West Midlands FS TKEL-HCB Angus
XRF304C		ET	65	80	Staffordshire Fire Brigade	SD Lammascote Rd-Stafford-1980 TKEL-HCB Angus
EWG942C		ET	65	81	Central Area Fire Brigade (Scotland)	Grangemouth Rd-Falkirk-1975 F3 Falkirk-Central Region FB-1981 TKEL-Dennis M
GPC909C		ET	65	83	Surrey County Council Fire Brigade	Addlestone Moor-Chertsey-1974 /ND 33 Chertsey-1983 TKEL-Wray
GPC910C		ET	65	83	Surrey County Council Fire Brigade	Ladymead-Guilford-1974/WD 22 Guilford-1983 TKEL-Wray

DDC999C	6	ET	65	78	Middlesbrough County Borough Fire Brigade	1 Park Road South-Middlesbrough-1968 2 South Rd-Norton-1974-Tee-side FB 2 Norton-Cleveland County FB-1978 TKEL-Dennis M
GXD488C		ET	65	83	Luton County Borough Fire Brigade	Studley Rd-Luton-1974 /O Luton-Bedfordshire FB-1975 **Converted Decontamination Unit-1983** TKEL-Dennis M
CFL887C EEW695C (Re-registered)		ET	65	84	Huntingdonshire & Peterborough FB	Dogsthorpe Rd-Peterborough-1974 N14 Peterborough-1980/Reserve-1984 Cambridgeshire Fire & Rescue Service TKEL-Dennis M
EFA650D		ET	66	82	Burton upon Trent County BFB	Burton upon Trent-1972 /High St-Burton-1974 SD Burton-1982-Staffordshire Fire Brigade TKEL-Dennis M
EDV562D		ET	66	82	Devon Fire Brigade	Newton Rd-Torquay-1974 /S17 Torquay-Devon FB-1984 TKEL-HCB Angus
HUO64D		ET	66 ,	84	Devon Fire Brigade	North Rd-Barnstaple-1974 /N1 North Rd-Barnstaple-1984 TKEL-HCB Angus
EMW683D		ET	66	84	Wiltshire Fire Brigade	4/1 Hilperton Rd-Trowbridge-1984 TKEL-HCB Angus
FBN650D		ET	66	81	Bolton County Borough Fire Brigade	Marsden Rd-Bolton-1970 /Moor Lane-Bolton-1974 B20 Bolton-1975 /D40 Whitehill St-Stockport-1981 Greater Manchester CFS TKEL-Dennis M
ULG998E		ET	67	78	Cheshire County Fire Brigade	B5 Mobberley Way-Knutsford-1974 /B3 Knutsford-1978 TKEL-Carmichael
DTU912F		ET	67	78	Cheshire County Fire Brigade	C1 Macon Way-Crewe-1978 TKEL-Dennis M
HTE554F	951	ET	67	78	Lancashire County Fire Brigade	11.1 Park Rd-Stretford-1974 /A15 Stretford-1975 A13 Liverpool Rd- Eccles 1978/Greater Manchester CFS TKHM-Albe
DJK999F	6	ET Salv/T	67	83	County Borough of Eastbourne Fire Brigade	Bourne St-Eastbourne-1974 B11 Bourne St-Eastbourne-1983-East Sussex FB TKEL-HCB Angus
GDY420F		ET Salv/T	68	85	Hastings County Borough Fire Brigade	Bohemia Rd-Hastings-1974 /B8 Hastings-East Sussex FB-1985 TKEL-HCB Angus
NED101G		**ERA** ET/SalvT	68	79	Warrington County Borough Fire Brigade	Winwick St-Warrington-1974 /B1 Warrington-Cheshire FB TKEL-HCB Angus-**Fitted pump**
MFG298G		ET	69	8x?	Fife Fire Brigade (Scotland)	Carnegie Rd-Dunfermline-1980 **Body to Dodge G13C-Methven&Thomson-EMS262V** TKEL-HCB Angus
RKE698G	400	ET	69	84	Kent Fire Brigade	AD Park Farm Rd-Folkestone-1974 A19 Folkestone-1984 KHL-HCB Angus
RKE699G	401	ET	69	86	Kent Fire Brigade	CD Loose Rd-Maidstone-1974 /C60 Maidstone-1986 KHL-HCB Angus
UKR396H	402	ET	69	86	Kent Fire Brigade	DD Upper Bridge St-Canterbury-1974 /D80 Canterbury-1986 KHL-HCB Angus
UKR397H	403	ET	69	86	Kent Fire Brigade	ED Cold Harbour Rd-Northfleet-1974 /E35 Northfleet-1986 KHL-HCB Angus
GPT235H	219	ET	70	88	Durham County Fire Brigade	B11Woodstone Villages-Fencehouses-1974 N4 Fencehouses-1988 TKEL-HCB Angus
OVV318J		Res/T	70	81	Northampton Fire Brigade	SD The Mounts-Northampton-1974-Northamptonshire FB CF350-NFB
KEM475K		ET	71	78	Bootle County Borough Fire Brigade	Strand Rd-Bootle-1974 /N1 Netherton-Bootle-1976 Reserve-1983-Merseyside FB TKEL-HCB Angus
BNV769K		Res/T	72	79	Northamptonshire Fire Brigade	B4 Staverton Rd-Daventry J2-Hawson

HCR815N		ET	74	92	City of Southampton	St Marys Rd-Southampton-1974/D54 St Mary's-Hampshire FB TKG-HCB Angus
HWK999N		Res/T	74	90	Warwick County Fire Brigade	ND 20 Newtown Rd-Nuneaton-1990 TKEL-HCB Angus
LEL356P		ET	76	87	Dorset Fire Brigade	A7 North Quay-Weymouth-1987 TKG-Cocker
LEL357P		ET	76	86	Dorset Fire Brigade	B18 Wimborne Rd-Poole-1986/**Written off in RTA** TKG-Cocker/
SDU755R		Res/T	77	90	Warwick County Fire Brigade	SD 29 Warwick St-Royal Leamington Spa-1990 TKEL-HCB Angus
YAC999S		Res/T	78	90	Warwick County Fire Brigade	ND 26 Corporation St-Rugby-1990 TKEL-HCB Angus
DDL999V		ET	80	91	Isle of Wight Fire Brigade	South St-Newport-1991 /**Converted Foam/Salvage-Date** TKG- HCB Angus
PRE442W		ET	80	90	Staffordshire Fire Brigade	SD High St-Burton upon Trent-1988 Reserve-1990 TKG-Benson
PRE443W		ET	80	90	Staffordshire Fire Brigade	ND Bethesda St-Hanley-Stoke-1987 Reserve-1990 TKG-Benson
PEX669W		ET	81	94	Norfolk Fire Service	A27 Bethel St-Norwich-1992 Reserve-1994 KG-Carmichael
UEW460X		ET/CU	82	91	Cambridgeshire Fire & Rescue Service	N27/A27 Hartford Rd-Huntingdon-1991 **Sold to Gloucestershire Bus Co as Air Cushion Rescue/U** KG-CMC
NGL848X		ET	82		Cornwall County Fire Brigade	7.1 Berrycombe Rd-Bodmin TKG-CFE
GEX533Y		ET	82		Norfolk Fire Service	**ex B47 Kilhams Way-Kings Lynn-1992** 54 Norwich Rd-Thetford- KG-Carmichael
HFE205Y		ET	82		Lincolnshire Fire Brigade	A1 South Park Ave-Lincoln TKG-Warner
JVL238Y		ET	83	96	Lincolnshire Fire Brigade	B5 Eastfield Rd-Louth TKG-HCB Angus
A648TFE		ET	83	96	Lincolnshire Fire Brigade	D10 Radcliffe Rd-Stamford KD-F&Wylie

Warwick County operated three Bedford TK Rescue Tenders that had HCB Angus bodied. This 1978 example, YAC999S, was photographed at Coleshill as a Hose Layer , its subsequent role. The others were based at Nuneaton and Royal Leamington Spa. The Fire Officer who had the main input into the look of this appliance took his design with him to his next command, as can be seen in the Rescue Tender's of the County of Avon FB of the late 1970s and early 1980s. *Clive Shearman*

A844WTU		ET	84	91	Mid Glamorgan Fire Service (Wales)	21 Dynevor St-Merthyr Tydfil-1991 **Sold to Cork County FB-Ireland** TL860-Saxon
WIA6938		ET	84		Northern Ireland Fire Brigade	**ex A01 Belfast Central-1989** /Reserve-Date TK1260-Alexander
WIA6939		ET	84		Northern Ireland Fire Brigade	**ex D07 Londonderry-1991**/D02 Crescent Link-Londonderry TK1260-Alexander
A619LWX		ET	84	?	West Yorkshire Fire Service	? TL570-Angloco
A987XCV		ET	84		Cornwall County Fire Brigade	2.1 College St-Camborne TKG-HCB Angus
A988XCV		ET	84	95	Cornwall County Fire Brigade	3.1 Trescobeas Rd-Falmouth **Scrapped following major engine defect.** TKG-HCB Angus
A463KBJ		ET	84	97	Suffolk Fire Service	A01 Colchester Rd-Ipswich -1996 Reserve- TKG-HCB Angus
A947RCK		ET	84	95	Lancashire County Fire Brigade	B70 Manchester Rd-Accrington TL860-Kendal
A948RCK		ET	84	95	Lancashire County Fire Brigade	B94 Bradley Rd-Nelson TL860-Kendal
B484DMB		ET	85	91	Mid Glamorgan Fire Service (Wales)	15 Oxford St-Trefforest-Pontypridd- 1991 **Sold to Cork County FB-Ireland** TL860-Saxon
B485DMB		ET	85	91	Mid Glamorgan Fire Service (Wales)	01 Sunnyside-Bridgend-1991/**Sold Cork County FB-Ireland** TL860-Saxon
B345DFW		Res/T	85	96	Lincolnshire Fire Brigade	A2 Nelson Sr-Gainsborough TL750-Saxon
C570LVL		Res/T	86	96	Lincolnshire Fire Brigade	C2 West Elloe Ave Spalding TL750-Saxon
C551JBO		Res/T	86	97	Gwent Fire Brigade-**1996** South Wales Fire Service (Wales)	B05 Cemetery Rd-Ebbw Vale-1995/Reserve- TL860-Saxon
C552JBO		Res/T	86	97	Gwent Fire Brigade-**1996** South Wales Fire Service (Wales)	B09 Malpas Rd-Newport -1995 /Reserve- TL860-Saxon
D927CRF		ET	87		Lothian & Borders Fire Brigade (Scotland)	34 Abbotsford Rd-Galashiels TL750-Excalibur CBK
D154SCX	111	ET	87	?	West Yorkshire Fire Service	? TL750-HCB Angus
D155SCX	112	ET	87	?	West Yorkshire Fire Service	**ex CD Outcote Rd-Huddersfield-1995**/ D Reserve- TL750-HCB Angus
D156SCX	113	ET	87	?	West Yorkshire Fire Service	BD Green Lane-Rawdon-Leeds TL750-HCB Angus
D118WTL		Res/T	87		Lincolnshire Fire Brigade	D9 Church Lane-Sleaford-1996 D10 Radcliffe Rd-Stamford TL750-HCB Angus
D810OBW		Res/T	86	96	Oxfordshire Fire Service	A06 Sterling Rd-Kidlington TKG-HCB Angus
E112GCW	30039	ET	86	97	Lancashire County Fire Brigade	**ex C54 Weldbank Rd-Rd-Chorley -1995**/ Training Centre- TL860-F&Wylie
E113GCW	30040	ET	86	95	Lancashire County Fire Brigade	A11 Cable St-Lancaster TL860-F&Wylie
BDZ871		ESU	87		Northern Ireland Fire Brigade	F09 Mill St-Irvinstown TL750-Alexander
EDZ2683		ESU	88		Northern Ireland Fire Brigade	F13 Thomas St-Dungannon CF350-Alexander
EDZ2685		ESU	88		Northern Ireland Fire Brigade	E02 Waveney Rd-Ballymena CF350-Alexander

EDZ2686		ESU	88		Northern Ireland Fire Brigade	F02 Mountjoy Rd-Omagh CF350-Alexander
EDZ2687		ESU	88		Northern Ireland Fire Brigade	B05 Valentia Place-Newcastle CF350-Alexander
EDZ2688		ESU	88		Northern Ireland Fire Brigade	E10 Fair Hill Rd-Magherafelt CF350-Alexander
EDZ2689		ESU	88		Northern Ireland Fire Brigade	D08 Lodge Rd-Coleraine CF350-Alexander
E174DVH	113	ET	88		West Yorkshire Fire Service	A Reserve TL850-Devcoplan

Many fine examples of Emergency Tenders were mounted on the Bedford TKEL chassis. A select number had the Dennis Miles bodywork as seen on CFL887C, which operated out of Dogsthorpe Road station in Peterborough. One feature of these appliances was the large window in the rear of the appliance. A feature of the two Huntingdonshire & Peterborough Fire Brigade ET's was that they were delivered with white livery. *Michael Lawmon*

					Bedford QL & RLHZ & TM & TK Recovery Vehicles	The early 2 Ton machines were powered by a 6 cylinder petrol engine. The QL 4x4 model was developed during the War, and at the start of the 1950's the 7ton S type became available in either the 4x2 s type or 4x4 R type.
EYU730		Rec/V	38	47	Tottenham Fire Brigade	The Green-Tottenham Bedford 2 Ton
DBY797		Rec/V	38	48	LCC London Fire Brigade	Bedford 2 Ton
DOY327	12.BL	Rec/V	38	56	LCC London Fire Brigade	Newport St Bedford 2 Ton
GYR99		Rec/V	45	61	Cornwall County Fire Brigade	Cornwall Workshops-Camborne Bedford QL
GYR137	203	Rec/V	45	65	Kent Fire Brigade	St Lawrence Farm-Old Dover Rd Canterbury-1960 W/S Pattenden Lane Marden Bedford QL
GYR145		Rec/V	45	63	Gloucestershire Fire Service	Lansdowne Rd-Cheltenham-1960 Keynsham Rd-Cheltenham-1963 Bedford QL
GYR147	202	Rec/V	45	60	Kent Fire Brigade	Market Place-Maidstone Bedford QL
GYR416		Rec/V	45	60	Durham County Fire Brigade	The Sands-Durham-1959 Finchale Rd-Framwellgate Moor-Durham-1960 **Crane re-chassied onto Bedford RLHZ 6567PT** Bedford QL
GYR417	15BL	Rec/V	45	64	Essex County Fire Service	34 Alfreds Way-Barking Workshops-1964 London FB -1965 Bedford QL
GYR418		Rec/V	45	66	Hertfordshire County Council Fire Brigade	Harpenden Rd-St Albans-1966 Bedford QL
GYR419		Rec/V	45	60	Essex County Fire Service	A2 Cowdrey Ave-Colchester Bedford QL
						All appliances below were fitted with a device called a stack grab. It was designed to tear apart haystacks.
GYR734		Rec/V	45	**64 ?**	West Riding of Yorkshire Fire Brigade	Shipley Fire Station Bedford QL
GYR740		Rec/V	45	**70 ?**	West Riding of Yorkshire Fire Brigade	Pontefract & Wetherby Fire Station's Bedford QL
GYR742		Rec/V	45	**70 ?**	West Riding of Yorkshire Fire Brigade	A11 Albert St-Harrogate-1960 Bedford QL
GYR807		Rec/V	45	**70 ?**	West Riding of Yorkshire Fire Brigade	Slaithwaite Fire Station Bedford QL
						The ALC registered series were ex AFS (Auxiliary Fire Service) machines. They are all RLHZ chassied machines.
368ALC		Rec/V	61	?	Hampshire Fire Service	Nutbeen Farm-Eastleigh-1964/#1 Hales St-Coventry-1974 City of Coventry /B3 Hales St-Coventry- West Midlands FS
370ALC		Rec/V	61	?	Essex County Fire Service	Barking Workshops
371ALC		Rec/V	61	78	Lancashire County Fire Brigade	8.1 Windermere Rd-Leigh-1967 Cheshire FB Workshops
372ALC		Rec/V	61	?	LCC London Fire Brigade	London FB Workshops-Ruislip-1965 Trowbridge Workshops Wiltshire Fire Brigade
373ALC		Rec/V	61	93	Devon County Fire Brigade	Devon FB Workshops /A4 College St-Camborne-1964 A4 College St-Camborne-1993/Cornwall County Fire Brigade
374ALC		Rec/V	61	84	Derbyshire Fire Service	Workshops
375ALC		Rec/V	61	83	City of Birmingham	10 Ettington Rd-Aston-1974 /A5 College Rd-Perry Bar-1983 West Midlands Fire Service
376ALC		Rec/V	61	?	Durham County Fire Brigade	Finchale Rd-Framwellgate Moor-Durham-1967 Home office Stores-1968/E9 By Pass Rd-Mold-Clwyd County
377ALC		Rec/V	61	92	Scottish Home Office Stores	Used as a snow plough at the end of its career.
9825WW		Rec/V	60	?	West Riding of Yorkshire Fire Brigade	Corporation St-Morley RLHZ-WRFB

6567PT		Rec/V	61	92	Durham County Fire Brigade	Finchale Rd-Durham- **Crane off Bedford QL-GYR416** **Sold to Willinghams Recovery Ltd-Durham** RLHZ-HCB
6091DF		Rec/V	63	75	Gloucestershire Fire Service	12 Keynsham Rd-Cheltenham-1974 RLHZ-Miles-Bates Holmes Crane
BBE739B		Rec/V	64	?	Lindsey County Fire Brigade	Workshops-1974 /**Trans Lincolnshire Fire Brigade-1975** **Trans Humberside FB-Yellow livery** RLHZ-HCB
SNK53D		Rec/V	66		Hertfordshire County Council Fire Brigade	Harpenden Way-St Albans-1974/Workshops- Bedford RSH-Dial Holmes
GTH284E		Rec/V	67	?	Carmarthen & Cardiganshire (Wales)	B07 Lime Grove Ave-Carmarthen-1974 A2 Carmarthen-1992 /Dyfed FB RLHZ-
CLG510S		Heavy ResV	78		Cheshire County Fire Brigade	B6 Ordenance Ave-Birchwood M-Boughton-Cheshire FB
YYA838X		Heavy ResV	81		Somerset Fire Brigade	Brigade Headquarters TK-Wreckers International
EMJ300Y		Rec/V	82		Buckinghamshire Fire Brigade	Brigade Workshops-Aylesbury TM-Wreckers International
A200DRR		Rec/V	84		Derbyshire Fire Service	Brigade Workshops TM-Wreckers International

Chassis					**Bedford Chassied Specialist Appliances**	**Engines**
		K	30s	40s	Weight	The Bedford range of vehicles were powered by a vast range
		QL	30s	50s	2 tons	of petrol and diesel engines from the early 6 cylinder petrol
		S	50s	60s	3 tons	up to the current Cummins and Perkins diesel engines . In
		TK	60	80s	7 Tons	1987 Bedford was sold to a British Company AWD Ltd (All
		KM	66	80s	2-16 Tons	Wheel Drive) . This was a short lived venture as they went
		CA	52	72	up to 24 Tons	into liquidation in 1992.
		TJ	62	76	10-12 cwt	
		CF	70s	80s	2- Tons	
		TL	80s		18-22-25-35 cwt	
		TM	80s		5- Tons	
					up to 38 Tons	
DJH319		HLL	37	60	Hertfordshire County Fire Brigade	B16 College Rd-Cheshunt K-HFB
DOY327	12.BL	Rec/V	38	56	LCC London Fire Brigade	D61 Lambeth Workshops K-
ANL314		Salv/T	39	68	Newcastle & Gateshead Joint Fire Brigade	**ex Pump-Amble-1958**/B1 Swinburne St-Gateshead-1964 B1 Dryden Rd-Gateshead-1968 K-N&GJFB
KMV600	ST-1	Salv/T	39	54	Tottenham Fire Brigade	The Green-Tottenham-1948-Middlesex FB ML-Limousine
FYR276	36-L	FOT	39	62	LCC London Fire Brigade	C42 Evelyn St-Deptford K-London FB
FYR285	45-L	FOT	39	62	LCC London Fire Brigade	D71 Este Rd-Battersea K-London FB
GYR819		WRC	45	?	Cambridgeshire Fire & Rescue Service	Churchill Rd-Wisbech QL-HOS
CDC111		FOT	52	62	Middlesbrough County Fire Brigade	#1 Park Rd South-Middlesbrough M-30cwt-TFB
VYT507		FOT	53	?	Pembrokeshire Fire Brigade (Wales)	**ex Petrol Tanker -1968** / High St-Pembroke Dock- ? S-
LYO788		Foam/C	53	92	County of Flintshire Fire Brigade (Wales)	By Pass Rd-Mold-1974/E9 By Pass Rd-Mold-1992 County of Clwyd FB RL-HOS/CCFB

THU700		FOT	54	71	City of Bristol	#3 St Andrews Rd-Avonmouth SH-Oldland
NYV627		HLL	55	84	Lindsey County Fire Brigade	C4 Pelham Rd-Immingham-1976-1984 /Humberside FB SP-HOS
NYV660		C/Unit	55	82	Auxillary Fire Service-**1968**	Robin Hoods Walk-Skegness-1974 C1 Robin Hoods Walk-Skegness-1982 Lincolnshire FB RLHZ-HOS
NYV662		C/Unit	55	77	Auxillary Fire Service-**1968**	Knolbeck Lane-Brampton-West Riding of Yorkshire-1974 Brampton-South Yorkshire County FS-1977 SP-HOS
NYV663		C/Unit	55	83	Auxillary Fire Service-**1968** (Scotland)	Harbour Rd-Inverness-1975-Northern Area FB A1 Harbour Rd-Inverness-1983-Highlands & Islands FB SP-HOS
NYR306		Sea Eqp/T	55	?	Auxillary Fire Service -**1968** (Wales)	**ex EP** / Rd-Holyhead-Angelsey County FB SP-HOS
NYR809		C/Unit	55	**82 ?**	Auxillary Fire Service-**1968**	A11 Albert St-Harrogate-1966/A11 Skipton Rd-Harrogate-West Riding of Yorkshire-1974 **Converted to Breathing App/T**-North Yorkshire FB-1982 SP-HOS
NYR820		C/Unit	55	76	Auxillary Fire Service-**1968**	Stafford Fire Station-1971 / Lammascote Rd-Stafford-1976 Staffordshire Fire Brigade SP-HOS
NYR824		C/Unit	55	81	Auxillary Fire Service-**1968**	#2 Castle Rd-Kidderminster-1974-Worcester City & County 24 Castle Rd-Kidderminster-**1977 ?** 26 Friar Street-Droitwich-1981-Hereford & Worcester FB SP-HOS
NYR857		C/Unit	55	81	Auxillary Fire Service-**1968** (Scotland)	Blackness Rd-Dundee-1975 Angus Area Fire Brigade A1 Blackness Rd-Dundee-1981-Tayside Fire Brigade SP-HOS
NYR963		Foam/C	55	67	Auxillary Fire Service -**1968** (Scotland)	Craigshill-Livingston- South Eastern Area FB SP-HOS
PCE829		WRC	55	77	Cambridgeshire Fire & Rescue Service	S1 Parkside-Cambridge-1967 / N20 Horsefair-Wisbech-1973 N18 Cemetery Rd-Whittlesley-1977 RL-Marshall
VHT646		HLL Salv/T	55	71	City of Bristol	Southmead Rd-Southmead-Bristol S-Oldland
VHY150		BAT	55	69	City of Bristol	#3 St Andrews Rd-Avonmouth TJ1-Hawson
VCY914		Salv/T	56	78	City of Swansea (Wales)	#1 Grove Place-Swansea-1974 5 Grove Place-Swansea-1978/West Glamorgan County FB TJ1-HCB
SED999		FOT	56	63	Warrington County Borough Fire Brigade	Heathside-Warrington RL-Marsden
RYX482		C/Unit	56	74	Auxillary Fire Service-**1968**	Loose Rd-Maidstone-Kent Fire Brigade SP-Home Office
RYX484		C/Unit	56	82	Dorset Fire Brigade	Holdenhurst Rd-Bournemouth-1974 B24 Bournemouth-1982 /Dorset Fire Brigade SP-HOS
PGW272		FOT	56	?	Auxillary Fire Service-**1968**	**ex AFS-EP** Worship St-Hull Central-1City of Kingston upon Hull FB-1974 A1 Hull Central- ? -Humberside Fire Brigade RLHZ-HOS-C of K u HFB
PGW368		FOT	56	78	Auxillary Fire Service-**1968** (Wales)	**ex AFS EP** / A5 Commercial Rd-Port Talbot-1974-GCFB 4 Commercial Rd-Port Talbot-1978/West Glamorgan CFB RLHZ-HOS
PGW608		FOT	56	78	Auxillary Fire Service-**1968** (Wales)	**ex AFS EP** / B4 Hazel Rd-Penarth-1974-Glamorgan CFB 6 Hazel Rd-Penarth-1978/South Glamorgan County FS RLHZ-HOS
RXP638		FOT	56	79	Auxillary Fire Service-**1968** (Wales)	**ex AFS EP** / Barry Fire Station-1974-1979-Glamorgan CFB South Glamorgan County FS RLHZ-HOS

Here is shown an example of the 1950s Bedford SP appliance which were used by numerous brigades for various roles after the Auxillary Fire Service was disbanded in 1968. Control Unit NYR824 served at Castle Road in Kidderminster for the old Worcester City and County Fire Brigade. It finished service at Droitwich after it become part of the Hereford & Worcester Fire Brigade. *Michael Lawmon*

RXP666		FOT	56	84	Auxillary Fire Service-**1968** (Wales)	**ex AFS EP** / Thomas St-Treharris-1974-Merthyr Tydfil CFB 19 Thomas St-Treharris-1984 /Mid Glamorgan FB RLHZ-HOS
RXP710		FOT	56	84	Auxillary Fire Service-**1968** (Wales)	**ex AFS EP** / C1 Oxford St-Pontypridd-1974-Glamorgan CFB 15 Oxford St-Pontypridd-1984 /Mid Glamorgan County FB RLIIZ-IIOS
SYH452		FOT	56	79	City of Cardiff (Wales)	**ex AFS EP** / #4 Heol y Nant-Whitchurch-1974-City of Cardiff 1 Adam St-Cardiff-South Glamorgan-1975 / **Sold to Powys FS** RLHZ-Hoskins

SAA518		FOT	57	66	Hampshire Fire Service	C29 Steele Close-Eastleigh S-Hampshire FS
TOM781	44	BL/ET BAT	57	80	City of Birmingham	1 Lancaster Circus-Central-1974 **Converted to Breathing Apparatus Tender** A1 Lancaster Circus-Central-1980-West Midlands Fire Service S-Wilsdon
439GTC	587	FOT	57	72	Lancashire County Fire Brigade	D60 Park Rd-Stretford SP-LCFB
440GTC		FOT	57	74	Lancashire County Fire Brigade	D62 Liverpool Rd-Eccles-1972 B34/C54 Weldbank Rd-Chorley-1974 SP-LCFB
SYH459	1079	P/HL	57	75	Liverpool Fire Brigade	Liverpool Speke Airport RLHZ-HOS
ABG776		Foam/C	58	63	Birkenhead County Borough Fire Brigade	**ex Ambulance** /Whetstone Lane-Charing Cross A22-Lomas
WAO568		FOT	58	?	Cumberland County Fire Brigade	**ex WRT**-Lazonby-1975 /Hensingham-Whitehaven-1977 Cumbria Fire Service TJ4L-HCB
VYT148		FOT	58	74	Warwick County Fire Brigade	**ex ESSO Tanker-Purchased 1970** N22 Park Rd-Coleshill-1974 S-Warwick CFB
WOX841	7	FOT	58	80	City of Birmingham	1 Lancaster Circus-Central-1974 A1 Lancaster Circus-Central-1980/West Midlands Fire Service S-Wilsdon
XWW606		FOT	59	74	West Riding of Yorkshire Fire Brigade	Beancroft Rd-Castleford SP-WRYFB
XWW607		FOT	59	78	West Riding of Yorkshire Fire Brigade	Knolbeck Lane-Brampton /Market Place-Penistone SP-WRYFB
SDF769		WRC	59	?	Gloucestershire Fire Service	12 Lansdowne Rd-Cheltenham-1960 12 Keynsham Rd-Cheltenham- RLHZ-GFS
900AFJ		WRC	60	?	City of Exeter	#1 Howell Rd-Exeter-**ex Petrol Tanker** RLHZ-EFB
URV409	15	FOT	60	74	City of Portsmouth Fire Brigade	#2 Copnor Rd-Copnor-1972-**Converted into Rescue Tender** #3 Wayte St-Cosham-1974 TJ1-Hawson
EFT280		FOT	61	81	Tynemouth Fire Brigade	Preston North Rd-Tynmouth-1974 H York Rd-Whitley Bay-1981 /Tyne & Wear MFB TKEL-HCB
SCX294		FOT Salv/T	61	?	Huddersfield County Borough Fire Brigade	Outcote Bank-Huddersfield TK-
335TMB		FOT	61	75	Cheshire County Fire Brigade	B4 Newby Drive-Altrincham-1974 D46 Brownly Rd-Wythenshawe-1975-Greater Manchester CFS TK-CCFB
953VTB		Hi-ex FOT	61	71	Lancashire County Fire Brigade	E70 Broadway-Chadderton TJ4L-Hawson
278XTB	771	C/Unit	61	78	Lancashire County Fire Brigade	E74 Bolton Rd-Agecroft-1974 A12 Bolton Rd-Agecroft-1978/Greater Manchester CFS TKEL-Craven-Homalloy
279XTB	772	C/Unit	61	90	Lancashire County Fire Brigade	B30/C52 Garstang Rd-Fulwood TKEL-Craven-Homalloy
225DTM		HLL FOT	61	78	Bedfordshire Fire Brigade	2 Brewers Hill Rd-Dunstable-1974 10 Dunstable Rd-Toddington-1978 TKEL-HCB
242LFC		CAV	61	76	Oxfordshire Fire Service	**ex Ambulance** / A06 Sterling Rd-Kidlington J1-Lomas
XDK464		Salv/T	62	74	Rochdale County Borough FB	Maclure Rd-Rochdale-1974 TJ-RCBFB

Hose Layer and Foam Tender 225DTM was built on a Bedford TKEL chassis and carries Hampshire Car Bodies bodywork and was located at Dunstable in Bedfordshire. The large use of unpainted alloy bodywork was Popular at the time. The appliance was photographed when the traditional bell was being replaced by the two tone horn. *Michael Lawmon*

Gloucestershire Fire & Rescue recently put on the run a new Leyland T60 chassied Water Carrier. This is illustrated on the cover of companion volume 1. Pictured here is SDF769 the earlier 1959 Bedford RLHZ that saw service at Keynsham Road in Cheltenham. This was a shop-built appliance on the robust RL 4x4 wheel drive chassis which saw widespread use by the armed services. *Keith Wardell collection*

OCP641		Pump Salv/T	61	71	Halifax Fire Brigade	Gibbert Street-Halifax ? / Skircoat Moor Rd-Halifax TJ4L-Miles-**Named Winifred Oxley**
657TD	776	CAV	62	90	Lancashire County Fire Brigade	B30/C52 Garstang Rd-Fulwood TKEL-Craven-Homalloy
YTP501	11	Salv/T	62	?	Portsmouth County Borough Fire Brigade	#1 Somers Rd-Southsea-1963 #2 Copnor Rd-Copnor-1972-**Converted Foam Carrier- ?** TJ1-Hawson
XDL561		FoT Salv/T	62	83	Isle of Wight Fire Brigade	1 South St-Newport /**ex WRT-East Cowes** TKEL-HCB
2117VB	6FT	FOT	62	77	Croydon County Borough Fire Brigade	Old Town-Croydon-1965 /H31 Old Town-Croydon-1977 London Fire Brigade TKEL-Carmichael
871SYB		H/FoT	62	82	Somerset Fire Brigade	01 Lisieux Way-Taunton TKEL-HCB
383HVP	54	FOT Salv/T	62	83	City of Birmingham	1 Lancaster Circus-Central-1974 C07 Icknield Port Rd-Ladywood-1980 D7 Alexander Rd-Tipton-1983 /West Midlands Fire Service TKEL-Craven
141VEH		FOT SALV	62	80	City of Stoke on Trent Fire Brigade	Hanley Fire Station-1965/ Hamil Rd-Burslem-1974/1980 Staffordshire Fire Brigade TKEL-HCB
TWC429		FOT	63	76	Essex County Fire Brigade	C24/53 High St-Hadleigh-1971 B30/C50 Hogg Lane-Grays-1976 TKEL-Sun
MWC945		HLL	63	84	Essex County Fire Brigade	B34 Rainsford Lane-Chelmsford **Body re-chassied onto Bedford TM -A352MVX** SP-Essex CFB
MWC946	8HL	HLL	63	79	Essex County Fire Brigade	Alfreds Way-Barking-1965 /L27 Alfreds Way-Barking-1979 London Fire Brigade SP-Essex CFB

999VHY, a 1964 vintage Bedford TKEL with Hampshire Car Bodies bodywork, was one of many of the model supplied in the early 1960s. This Foam Carrier served at Brislington in Bristol. An identical machine was delivered to the North Riding of Yorkshire Fire Brigade at Grangetown, though that machine was subsequently written off in an accident after being transfered to the newly formed Tees-side FB in 1968.
Keith Wardell collection

8101ED		FOT	63	78	Warrington County Borough Fire Brigade	Heathside-Warrington-1968/Winwick St-Warrington-1974 B1 Winweick St-Warrington-1978/Cheshire County FB TKEL-Busmar
321FWW		HLL	63	78	West Riding of Yorkshire Fire Brigade	Lister St-Brighouse-1974 /B12 Lister St-Brighouse-1978 West Yorkshire Fire Service KM-
VGR555	No-15	FOT	63	74	Sunderland Fire Brigade	#1 Dun Cow St-Sunderland-1965 #3 Holborn Rd-Grindon-1974 TKEL-
XUD179		C/Unit	63	76	Oxfordshire Fire Service	ex Ambulance / A06 Sterling Rd-Kidlington J1-Lomas
531VBJ		BA Comp	64	87	Suffolk & Ipswich Fire Brigade	A01 Colchester Rd-Ipswich-Suffolk Fire Service J1-Williams & James
999VHY	1502	Foam/C	64	?	City of Bristol	#4 Bonville Rd-Brislington TKEL-HCB
BWN943B		Foam/C	64	78	City of Swansea (Wales)	#3 Woodfield St-Morriston-1969 /#3 Snay St-Morriston-1974 8 Snay St-Morriston-1978/West Glamorgan County FB TJ1-Hawson
AVN924B	47	FOT	64	82	North Riding of Yorkshire Fire Brigade	ex WRT / A8 Yarm-1974/80 7 Seaton Carew Rd-Billingham-1984-Cleveland County FB TJ5-HCB
ACK899B	261	FOT	64	78	Preston County Borough Fire Brigade	Blackpool Rd-Preston-1974 C50 Blackpool Rd-Preston-1978/Lancashire County FB TKEL-Pyrene
CCJ581B		WRC	64	72	Herefordshire County Fire Brigade	St Owen St-Hereford TKEL-HCB
GYL32C		Foam/C	64	95	County of Flintshire Fire Brigade (Wales)	Bradley Rd-Rhyl-1974 W1 Bradley Rd-Rhyl-County of Clwyd FB RLHZ-HOS/CCFB

Bedford TKEL Foam Tender EOM313C has Pyrene bodywork and served two owners. New to the London Road station in Langley in 1965, then part of Buckinghamshire before it passed to Royal Berkshire in 1974. The appliance had a unique appearance, and was built by a company with a long history of supplying premium Foam and Airport Crash Tenders to the aviation industry.
Keith Wardell collection

Reg	No	Type	In	Out	Brigade	Location/History
4398OZ		FOT	65	?	Northern Ireland Fire Brigade	? TK-Pyrene
DNW639C		FOT	65	78	Leeds City Fire Brigade	Dewsbury Rd-Hunslett-1974 E11 Dewsbury Rd-Hunslett-1978/West Yorkshire Fire Service TK-HCB Angus
CEW600C (later EEW694C)		WRC	65	88	Cambridgeshire Fire & Rescue Service	N27 Hartford Rd-Huntingdon-1972 / N17 Main St-Yaxley-RL-HCB Angus
EOM313C		FOT	65	80	Buckinghamshire Fire Brigade	19 London Rd-Langley-1974 E18 London Rd-Langley-1980/Royal Berkshire F&RS TKEL-Pyrene
EVJ224C		WRC	65	83	Herefordshire County Fire Brigade	St Mary St-Ross on Wye-1974 44 Gloucester Rd-Ross on Wye-1983 TKEL-Carmichael
EUE104C		C/Unit	65	85	Warwick County Fire Brigade	ex ET-1977 /Warwick St-Royal Leamington Spa TKEL-HCB Angus/Benson
CDR999C		F/HL	65	86	City of Plymouth	Crownhill Rd-Plymouth-1974 W49 Crownhill Rd-Plymouth-1986/Devon Fire Brigade TK-Mumford
GXD488C		CI/Unit	65	83	Luton County Borough Fire Brigade	ex Res/T-Studley Rd-Luton-1974 Converted Decontamination Unit 0 Studley Rd-Luton-1983 /Bedfordshire Fire Brigade TKEL-Dennis M
KKA339D	1062	F/HL	65	81	Liverpool Fire Brigade	Liverpool Speke Airport-1974/Merseyside Fire Brigade-1981 RLHZ-Pyrene
GHR863D		FOT	66	?	Wiltshire Fire Brigade	3/1 Ashley Rd-Sailsbury TK-Lee Motors
HPY117D	23	FOT	66	69	North Riding of Yorkshire Fire Brigade	A1 Middlesbrough Rd-Grangetown-1968-Tees-side FB Written off in RTA TKEL-HCB Angus
GHR843D		F/HL	66	?	Wiltshire Fire Brigade	4/6 Southbroom Rd-Devizes TKEL-HCB Angus
ECG767D		Foam Tanker	66	89	Hampshire Fire Service	B15/18 Privett Rd-Gosport TKEL-Hampshire FS
GBA447D		FOT	66	80	City of Salford	The Crescent-Salford-1974 A10 The Crescent-Salford-1975 A15 Park Rd-Stretford-1980/Greater Manchester CFS TKEL-Pyrene
LAL999E		C/Unit Salv/T	67	86	Nottinghamshire Fire Brigade	Rosemary St-Mansfield-1974 A1 Rosemary St-Mansfield-1986/Nottinghamshire Fire Service TKEL-Carmichael Preserved
HOR853E		Foam Tanker	67	89	Hampshire Fire Service	A1 West Ham Close-Basingstoke-1976 D58 Falconer Court-Fawley-1989 TKEL-Hampshire FS
JHA999E		FOT Salv/T	67	80	Smethwick & West Bromwich Fire Brigade	Oldbury Fire Station-1974 D1 Old Park Lane-Oldbury-1980/West Midlands Fire Service TJ-Hawson
JFS741E		FOT Salv/T	67	82	South Eastern Area Fire Brigade (Scotland)	Macdonald Rd-Edingburgh-Calder Rd-Sighthill-Marionville Drive-Marionville-1982 Lothian & Borders FB-Yellow livery TKHL-HCB Angus
JVD103E		Salv/T	67	80	Lanarkshire Fire Brigade (Scotland)	Dellburn St-Motherwell-1975 E02 Dellburn St-Motherwell- 1980 Strathclyde Fire Brigade TK-Hawson
JVD562E		Salv/T	67	?	Lanarkshire Fire Brigade (Scotland)	Main St-Coatbridge-1975 E04 Main St-Coatbridge- Strathclyde Fire Brigade TK-Hawson
RYF432E		Foam Tanker	67	88	Suffolk County Fire Service	A01 Colchester Rd-Ipswich TKM-SCFB

HVE939F		WRC	67	85	Cambridgeshire Fire & Rescue Service	S1 Parkside-Cambridge-1972/N20 Horsefair-Wisbech-1985 TKEL-Sun
MKL109F		WRC	68	?	Kent Fire Brigade	A11 Canterbury Rd-Ashford TKEL-Kent FB
MFG298G		ET C/Unit	68	80	Fife Fire Brigade (Scotland)	Carnegie Rd-Dunfermline /**Body transferred to** **Dodge G13C-Methven & Thomson-EMS262V** TKEL-HCB Angus
OFU733G		Foam Tanker	68	84	Lindsey County Fire Brigade	Pelham Rd-Immingham-1974 C4 Pelham Rd-Immingham-1984 /Humberside Fire Brigade KM-HCBAngus **6x4 WD**
NUN324G		FOT	68	79	Denbighshire & Montgomery (Wales)	Abergele Rd-Colwyn Bay-1974-Clwyd Fire Service TJ1-Hawson
YYN387H		WRC	70	85	Derbyshire Fire Service	Campton Grove-Buxton TKM-Butterfield
ALT466H		CIU	70	85	Fire Service College	**ex Salv/T** / Moreton in Marsh-Gloucestershire TK-Plaxton
ALT467H		C/Unit	70	85	Fire Service College	Moreton in Marsh-Gloucestershire **Sold to Cork County Irish Republic** TK-Plaxton
ALT471H		HLL Salv/T	70	84	Fire Service College	Moreton in Marsh-Gloucestershire TK-Plaxton
AMY708H		WRC	70	91	West Sussex Fire Brigade	07 Maltravers Rd-Littlehampton **Tank re-chassied onto Ford Cargo 1721-H197GKM** TKEL-West Sussex FB
MDR999H		FOC	70	86	City of Plymouth	Crownhill Rd-Plymouth-1974 W49 Crownhill Rd-Plymouth-1986 /Devon Fire Brigade TJ1-Hawson

The Bedford TK chassis was a popular chassis for specialist appliances of all types, though Mumford bodywork was less common and is seen here on Hose Layer and Foam Tender CDR999C at Crownhill, Plymouth. This appliance provided service for well over twenty years before it was replaced by a 4x4 Dodge G13 with Saxon bodywork.
Ken Reid

PNH808J		C/Unit	70	85	Northamptonshire Fire Brigade	**ex Mobile Library** / Moulton Way-Moulton-1985 TKEL-York,Ward & Rowlett
WKT646J		HLL	71	88	Kent Fire Brigade	B45 High St-Sittingbourne TKEL-Keam
WKT647J		HLL	71	88	Kent Fire Brigade	B39 Gravesend Rd-Strood TKEL-Keam
WKT648J		FOT	71	88	Kent Fire Brigade	A16 Ladywell-Dover TKEL-Keam
WKT649J		FOT	71	88	Kent Fire Brigade	B39 Gravesend Rd-Strood TKEL-Keam
BHW486J	2102	CIU Salv/T	71	86	City of Bristol	Speedwell Rd-Speedwell-Bristol-1974 / B6 Speedwell-1976 B4 Bonville Rd-Brislington-1986/County of Avon FB TKEL-Taylors
KUP381J	050	FOT	70	87	Durham County Fire Brigade	**ex Crook WRT-1978** / D4/S4 Watling St-Bishops Auckland TKEL-HCB Angus
EHW746K		C/Unit	71	86	City of Bristol	#1 Bridewell St-Bristol-1973/#1 Temple Back-Central-1974 A1 Temple Back-Central- 1986/County of Avon FB TKEL-Oldland
EHW747K	2101	HLL	71	86	City of Bristol	Southmead Rd-Bristol-1974 A2 Southmead Rd-Bristol-1986/County of Avon FB KC-Oldland
ABE647K		Foam Tanker	72	**75 ?**	Lindsey County Fire Brigade	Nelson St-Gainsborough-1974-Lincolnshire-1975 **Sold to the Northern Ireland Fire Authority** KM-HCB Angus-**6x4 WD**
TUP738K	215	C/Unit	72	95	Durham County Fire Brigade	Finchale Rd-Framwellgate Moor-Durham VAM-Northern Assemblies
TUP739K	216	CAV	72	94	Durham County Fire Brigade	Finchale Rd-Framwellgate Moor-Durham VAM-Northern Assemblies
XVJ229K		WRC	72	82	Hereford County Fire Brigade	St Owen St-Hereford-1974/46 St Owen St-Hereford-1982 Hereford & Worcester FB TKEL-Sun/Carmichael
PTK853K		FOT	72	84	Dorset Fire Brigade	B17 Blandford Rd-Hamworthy-1983-**Workshops- ?** TJ1-Hawson
RFX133K		CAV	72	82	Dorset Fire Brigade	B24 Holdenhurst Rd-Bornmouth-1982 A7 North Quay-Weymouth- TJ1-Hawson
JLT4K	CAV-4	CAV	72	?	GLC London Fire Brigade	J28 High St-Southgate CF 350-Locomotor
DTV999L		C/Unit	72	?	City of Nottingham	#1/B18 Shakespeare St-Nottingham-**Written off in RTA** CF350-
YUN129L		Hi-ex FOT	72	77	Denbighshire & Montgomery (Wales)	Bradley Rd-Wrexham-1974 /E1 Bradley Rd-Wrexham-1977 County of Clwyd FB CF350-CCFB
NHO554L		CAV	73		Hampshire Fire Service	C30 North Walls-Winchester TK-Hampshire FBWS
BSG653L		C/Unit	73	84	South Eastern Area Fire Brigade (Scotland)	Lauriston Place-Edingburgh- ? / MacDonald Rd-Edingburgh- ? Kirk Brae-Liberton-1984/Lothian & Borders FB TKG-SMT
WJE265L		WRC	73	96	Cambridgeshire Fire & Rescue Service	**ex B01 Cambridge-1987**/A17 Main St-Yaxley-1996 KM-HCB Angus
NSW277M		BAT	73	94	South Western Area Fire Brigade (Scotland)	D1 Brooms Rd-Dumfries-1975/94-Dumfries & Galloway CC TK-D&GFB
TLO100M	FEL-1	FELU	74	?	GLC London Fire Brigade	B21 Old Town-Clapham CF 350-Locomotor
WYD470M		WRC	74	89	Somerset Fire Brigade	02 Salmon Parade-Bridgewater TK-Wincanton
PNX999M		FOT	74	91	Warwick County Fire Brigade	N22 Park Rd-Coleshill **Tank re-chassied onto Dennis DFS-J904VRW**

						TKEL-HCB Angus
HA9823		FOT	75	?	Northern Ireland Fire Brigade	? TK-Lindsey
LVL227P		WRC	76	89	Lincolnshire Fire Brigade	C8 Station Rd-Long Sutton-1988 C2 West Elloe Rd-Spalding-1989 -Written off in RTA TL-Carmichael
LYD288P		WRC	76	92	Somerset Fire Brigade	21 Reckleford-Yeovil TK-Wincanton
MRB728P		C/Unit	76	83	Nottinghamshire Fire Service	B18 Shakespeare St-Nottingham TKEL-HCB Angus
KOW286P		BAT	76		Hampshire Fire Service	A1 West Ham Close-Basingstoke-1986 **Converted ET** /A1 Basingstoke-1990 VAS-Hampshire FS
YBW66R		PMover HLL/CAV	76	87	Oxfordshire Fire Service	A06 Sterling Rd-Kidlington TK750-Powell Duffryn
YBW67R		PMover CU/DCU	76	87	Oxfordshire Fire Service	A06 Sterling Rd-Kidlington TK750-Powell Duffryn
MBK390R		C/Unit	77		Hampshire Fire Service	C29 Steele Close-Eastleigh VAS-Hampshire
TMB502R		C/Unit	77	90	Cheshire County Fire Brigade	A1 Northgate St-Chester-1985 /A3 Ship St-Frodsham-1990 TKEL-Bo-alloy
UDT506S		C/Unit	77	89	South Yorkshire County Fire Service	D4 Highwoods Rd-Mexborough TK-Reebur
VDF860S	503	PMover DCU	78	95	Gloucestershire Fire & Rescue Service	**ex WRL 17 Moreton in Marsh**/12 Keynsham Rd- Cheltenham TKG-Mcdonald Kane-Torton
UVP97S	140	BAT C/Unit	78		West Midlands Fire Service	A1 Lancaster Circus-Central /Reserve- KG-Anglo
GUD226S		PMover	78	87	Oxfordshire Fire Service	B1 Rewley Rd-Oxford TK-Powell Duffryn
WWR611S		CCU	78	93	West Yorkshire Fire Service	C14 Huddersfield Rd-Dewsbury TK-Cocker
TPJ624S		WRC FOC	78	93	Surrey Fire Brigade	19 Eastbourne Rd-Godstone M-Surrey FB
TPJ625S		WRC FOC	78	93	Surrey Fire Brigade	27 London Rd-Camberley M-Surrey FB
TPJ626S		WRC FOC	78	93	Surrey Fire Brigade	35 Goose Green-Gomshall M-Surrey FB
TPJ627S		WRC FOC	78	93	Surrey Fire Brigade	25 West St-Haselmere M-Surrey FB
TPJ628S		WRC FOC	78	93	Surrey Fire Brigade	15 Hersham Rd-Walton on Thames M-Surrey FB
TPJ629S		WRC FOC	78	93	Surrey Fire Brigade	14 Gavell Rd-Painshill M-Surrey FB
YPV380S		PM/CIU CAV/FOC	78		Suffolk Fire Service	A14 Normanhurst Rd-Lowestoft -**also Breathing Apparatus** TK-Powell Duffryn
BGB901S		Salv/T	78	91	Strathclyde Fire Brigade (Scotland)	**ex Glasgow Salvage Corps-1984** D5 Corsehill Mount Rd-Dreghorn TK-Fulton & Wylie
LVH196T		C/Unit	78		East Sussex Fire Brigade	A01 North St-Lewes YMT-Anglo
HFE924T		PMover	79	96	Lincolnshire Fire Brigade	A1 South Park Ave-Lincoln TK-Rolonoff-Powell Duffryn
HFW777T		PMover	79		Lincolnshire Fire Brigade	C1 Robin Hoods Walk-Boston TK-Rolonoff-Powell Duffryn
DDF940T	538	PMover ISU	79	95	Gloucestershire Fire & Rescue Service	**ex WRL 12 Cheltenham**/21 Chesterton Lane-Cirencester TKG-Mcdonald Kane-Torton
YAP559T		FOT	79		East Sussex Fire Brigade	A06 Fort Rd-Newhaven TK-Freight Developments
HHS924T	A019	Salv/T	79		Strathclyde Fire Brigade	**ex Glasgow Salvage Corps-1984**

						(Scotland)	A01 Port Dundas Rd-Cowcaddens-Glasgow TK-F&Wylie
HPP183V		C/Unit	79	93	Hertfordshire County Council Fire Brigade	B18 Wellfield Rd-Hatfield TK860-Longwell Green
JFH318V		PMover Display/U	79	95	Gloucestershire Fire & Rescue Service	ex WRL 05 Gloucester /Brigade Headquarters-Cheltenham TKG-Mcdonald Kane-Torton
JFH319V		PM over ICU	79	95	Gloucestershire Fire & Rescue Service	ex WRL 05 Gloucester /05 Eastern Ave-Gloucester TKG-Mcdonald Kane-Torton
HGV218V		PM/CIU CAV/FOC BAT	79		Suffolk Fire Service	B01 Fornham Rd-Bury St Edmonds TK-Powell Duffryn
JBJ60V		PM/CIU FOC/CAV	80		Suffolk Fire Service	A01 Colchester Rd-Ipswich TK-Powell Duffryn
DDL999V		FOT Salv/T	80		Isle of Wight Fire & Rescue Service	ex ET-01/01 South Shore-Newport 03 York Ave-East Cowes- TK-Sparshatts
MUS920V	F076	Salv/T	80		Strathclyde Fire Brigade (Scotland)	ex Glasgow Salvage Corps-1984 F07 Castle Green St-Dumbarton TK-F&Wylie
GHN545V	1	PMover C/Unit	80		North Yorkshire Fire Brigade	ex D/S1 Clifford St-York-1987 A6/W2 Stonebridge Gate-Ripon TK1260-HCB Angus-Ray Smith
RVW836W		C/Unit	80		Essex County Fire Brigade	Brigade Headquarters/ Reserve- KG-Benson
JDL997W		WRC	80		Isle of Wight Fire Brigade	Tank Re-chassied off Ford Thames Trader-CDL306B 03 York Ave-East Cowes- ? / 04 Station Street-Ryde- KM-IoWFB
PRE441W	534	Damage Limitation Unit	80		Staffordshire Fire & Rescue Service	ex Foam/Salvage Tender-Burslem-1994 SD Moor St-Burton upon Trent TKG-Benson

Foam Tender PNX999M was photographed at Coleshill where it served as part of the Warwick County Fire Brigade. Coleshill has a busy risk area which includes the National Exhibition Centre and Birmingham International Airport. In the background is the Dennis DFS Prime Mover which replaced it. The tank from this 1974 appliance was made into a Prime Mover pod in 1991.
Clive Shearman

This Bedford TM water carrier A561LRE with Carmichael bodywork was photographed at Kidsgrove in Staffordshire. It now serves at Leek, while its sister serves at Cannock to the south of the county. The capacity of the water tank is 6700 litres (1500 gallons). Can you imagine taking an appliance this big on a 96 mile round trip '999' call to a 10 pump fire in Shropshire? That is what Leading Firefighter David Smith did when he was serving at Cannock, when the call came for another water carrier.
Clive Shearman

COMMER

Reg No	Fleet No	TYPE	YR	OS	Appliance & Brigade Name	Details/Stations
					Commer Chassied **Turntable Ladders**	
5222AC		TL	58	72	Warwick County Fire Brigade	Warwick St-Royal Leamington Spa-1967 Corporation St-Rugby-1972 **Preserved in Australia** 86A Haydon-Magirus-DL30H-100'L
OSD558		TL	60	78	South Western Area Fire Brigade (Scotland)	Kilmarnock-South Western Area FB- 1974 D02 Kilmarnock-Strathclyde FB-1978 **L Re-ch onto S& Drewry WY-XGG732S-Strathclyde FB** C7-Haydon-Magirus-100'L
113LKE	198	TL	60	80	Kent Fire Brigade	B Div-Wrotham Rd-Gravesend **Re-ch ladder to Dennis F125/KKE821V** Haydon-Magirus-100'L
792TKX		TL	61	79	Buckinghamshire Fire Brigade	London Rd-Langley-Buckinghamshire FB-1974 London Rd-Langley -Berkshire & Reading FB-1979 **Ladders Re-ch onto Ford D1114-Carmichael-YJM102T** **Royal Berkshire Fire Brigade** 86A Haydon-Magirus-100'L
430PKO	190	TL	61	82?	Kent Fire Brigade	A Div-Ladywell-Dover Haydon-Magirus-100'L
886NKL	189	TL	62	80	Kent Fire Brigade	C Div-Loose Rd-Maidstone Haydon-Magirus-100'L
USD443		TL	62	81	South Western Area Fire Brigade (Scotland)	Ayr Fire Station - 1972 - Brooms Rd-Dumfries-1975 D1 Brooms Rd-Dumfries-Dumfries & Galloway FB-1981 **Ladder re-ch onto Dodge G16C-Carmichael-YSM430W** Haydon-Magirus-100'L
BHH385B		TL	64	81	Carlisle City Fire Brigade	Warwick St-Carlisle CFB-1974-Cumbria FS-1981 **Ladder Re-chassied onto Dodge G16C/ Carmichael** **LHH678W -Cumbria Fire Service** C7-Haydon-Magirus-100'L

Commer 86A type Turntable Ladder 792TKX was new in 1959 to the Langley fire station in Buckinghamshire and was fitted with David Haydon bodywork and a Magirus 33-metre ladder.
In 1974 it passed to the Royal Berkshire Fire Service where it served a further five years. It is seen outside the Tuns Lane station in Slough.
Keith Wardell collection

					Commer Chassied Hydraulic Platforms	
356HWO		HP	63	80	Monmouthshire Fire Brigade (Wales)	New Rd-New Inn-Pontypool-1974 Hennllys Way-Cwmbran-1980 /Gwent FB **First HP in United Kingdom** VAC-Buttons-Simon SS65
890XNY		HP	64	85	Glamorgan County Fire Brigade (Wales)	Sunnyside-Bridgend-1969 B4 Hazel Rd- Penarth-Glamorgan CFB-1974 Hazel Rd-Penarth-South Glamorgan FB-1985 **Delivered as 65' and converted to 50' platform in 1970's** VAC-Evans-Simon-SS65
ATX400B		HP	64	72	Glamorgan County Fire Brigade (Wales)	C1 Oxford St-Trefforest-Pontypridd-1972 **Written off in RTA-pre merger** VAC-Evans-Simon-SS65
DTG101C		HP	65	79	Glamorgan County Fire Brigade (Wales)	A1 Cimla St-Neath-Glamorgan CFB-1974 Cimla St-Neath-West Glamorgan FB-1979 **Booms Re-chassied onto Dennis F125-Dennis-YEP817T** VAC-Evans-Simon-SS65
USD969K		HP	71	86	South Western Area Fire Brigade (Scotland)	Station Rd-Ayr-1975 D01 Station Rd-Ayr-1986 /Strathclyde Fire Brigade **The Orbitor had a maximum working height of 21.9** **(72ft).** C7-F&Wylie-Orbitor-72'

					Commer chassied Emergency/Rescue Tenders	
NPK992	12-ET ET-12 CU-2	ET	49	68	Surrey County Council Fire Brigade	Wimbledon Fire Station-1965 **Converted to C/Unit-1965** /Reserve-1968 / London FB QX-
NPK993		ET	49	70	Surrey County Council Fire Brigade	Chertsey Fire Station QX-
HDW93		Res/T	51	75	Newport County Borough FB (Wales)	Dock St-Maplpas-Newport-1969/Malpas Rd-Newport-1974 B9 Malpas-Gwent FB-1975 QX-Miles
NAT164		Res/T	52	69	City of Kingston upon Hull Fire Brigade	#1 Worship St-Central-Hull-1969 QX-Cuerdon
MHE999		ET	?	71	Barnsley County Borough Fire Brigade	QX-Miles
OPA861		ET	?	65	Surrey County Council Fire Brigade	Guilford Fire Station QX-
VTJ929		Res/T	55	70	Lancashire County Fire Brigade	11.1 Manchester Rd-Stretford-1968 Reserve-1970 QX 44A-Cuerdon
EM6210		Res/T	55	72	Bootle County Borough Fire Brigade	Strand Rd-Bootle-1972/**Preserved** QX-Miles
RTV999		Res/T	56	72	City of Nottingham	#1 Shakespeare St-Nottingham-1972 QX-Carmichael
3663U		ET	57	?	Leeds City Fire Brigade	Park Street- Leeds Central QX-Jennings
PJV506		ET	59	72	Grimsby County Borough FB	#1 Peakes Lane-Grimsby FC1500-GFB
LTS885		Res/T	60	78	Angus Area Fire Brigade (Scotland)	Strathmore Ave-Dundee-1975 A02 Strathmore Ave -Dundee/Tayside FB-1978 QX-Carmichael
27WMX	ET.4	ET	60	73	Middlesex Fire Brigade (Ambulance Service)	A1 Church St Edmonton 1965/**Converted to Control Unit** G30 Harrow Rd-Wembley/London FB-1973 QX-Middlesex FB
28WMX	GPL-1	Hose/FT	60	72	Middlesex Fire Brigade (Ambulance Service)	? -**Converted to ET in 1968** QX-Middlesex FB

2598MV	ET.5	ET	60	73	Middlesex Fire Brigade (Ambulance Service)	C65 London Rd-Heston-1965/D27 Heston-1972/Reserve-1973 QX-Middlesex FB	
4130SF		ET	62	85	Scottish Fire Service Training School (Scotland	Gullane QX-Carmichael	
TCJ521		Res/T	63	76	Hereford County Fire Brigade	St Owen St-Hereford-1974 W46 Hereford-Hereford & Worcester FB-1976 72A-HCB-Hereford CFB	
148DDM		Res/T	63	77	County of Flintshire Fire Brigade (Wales)	Coast Rd-Rhyl-1965 By Pass Rd-Mold-1967/Chester Rd-Queensferry-1972 Chester Rd-Deeside-1974/E2 Deeside-Clwyd FS-1977 QX-HCB	
123XNY		Res/T	64	75	Glamorgan County Fire Brigade (Wales)	B1 Sunnyside-Bridgend-1974 W1 Bridgend-Mid Glamorgan FS-1975 Vac-Dennis M	
DTG102C		Res/T	65	79	Glamorgan County Fire Brigade (Wales)	A1 Cimla St-Neath-1974/1 Neath-1979-West Glamorgan FS Vac-Evans	
DTG103C		Res/T	65	75	Glamorgan County Fire Brigade (Wales)	C1 Oxford St-Trefforest-Pontypridd-1974 15 Pontypridd-Mid Glamorgan FB-1975 Vac-Evans	
CDM593C		Res/T	65	77	County of Flintshire Fire Brigade (Wales)	Coast Rd-Rhyl-1974/W1 Coast Rd-Rhyl-1977-Clwyd FS Vac-HCB Angus	
FPP562C		Res/T	65	80	Buckinghamshire Fire Brigade	14 Sherwood Drive-Bletchley-Milton Keynes-1974 Vac-John Morris	
BVV331C		Res/T	65	79	Northamptonshire Fire Brigade	The Mounts-Northampton-1970 10 Irthlingborough Rd-Wellingborough 1979 FC 1500 cwt-Lomas	
JDB999E		Res/T	66	76	Stockport County Borough Fire Brigade	#1 Whitehall St-Stockport-1974 D40 Whitehall St-1976/Greater Manchester CFS Vac-Kerbell	
KES313F		Res/T	67		Perth & Kinross Fire Brigade (Scotland)	High St-Perth-1975/B1 Perth-Tayside FB-1986 **Sold to Fire Service School-Gullane** Vac-Carmichael	
EHB680G		Res/T	68	78	Merthyr Tydfil Fire Brigade (Wales)	#1 Dynevor Rd-Merthyr-1974 21 Merthyr-Mid Glamorgan-1975 15 Pontypridd-1978-Mid Glamorgan Vac-Dennis M	
LTT197P	5168	Res/T	75		Devon Fire & Rescue Service	**ex WRL**/ Reserve-Commando RG11-HCB Angus/DF&RS	

					Commer KC40 Chassied Specialist Appliances	The KC 40 Walk Thru van was introduced in 1961. It had a payload of 1.5-3 tons so it made it an ideal base for light specialist appliances. The heavier models were distinct as they had twin rear wheels. It was powered by a Rootes diesel engine. Badged as a Dodge from 1977, it was later replaced by the Dodge S Series	
5001DN		Salv/T	62	73	City of York	Clifford St-York KC40-Russell-**Yellow livery**	
313FLM	CAV.3	CAV	64	80	London Fire Brigade	D61/B22 Albert Embankment-1970 E21 High St-Lewisham-1980 KC40-Strachan	
CEM683		Decon/U	64	?	Bootle County Borough Fire Brigade	Strand Rd-Bootle- ? KC40 Air Van-BCBFB	
AFB628B		HLL	64	75	City of Bath	Cleveland Bridge-Bath-1974/B1 Cleveland Bridge-Bath-1975 **Conv Canteen Van** /B7 Kingswood-1983-County of Avon KC40-CoBFB	
AJT445B		Res/T	64	76	Dorset Fire Brigade	A7 North Quay-Weymouth KC40-	
AJT446B		Res/T	64	76	Dorset Fire Brigade	B18 Wimborne Rd-Poole KC40-	

LRF595B		FOT Salv/T	64	74	Staffordshire Fire Brigade	Old Hednesford Rd-Cannock KC40-SFB
LRF596B		FOT Salv/T	64	77	Staffordshire Fire Brigade	Alexander Rd-Tipton-1974/D7 Alexander Rd-Tipton-1977 West Midlands Fire Service KC40-SFB
CPT943B		WRU	64	78	Durham County Fire Brigade	Finchale Rd-Frawellgate Moor-Durham KC40-DCFB
EUD999C		ET	65	78	Oxfordshire Fire Service	C01 The Broadway Didcot KC40-Air Drive
AHF629C		ET	65	72	Wallasey County Borough Fire Brigade	Mill Lane-Liscard-Wallasey Merseyside KC40-WCB FB
BEO359C		CIU	65	87	Barrow in Furrness CBFB	Abbey Rd-Barrow in Furness-1974 W11 Hensingham-Whitehaven-1987 Cumbria Fire Service KC40-CCFB
ENR200C		FoT	65	84	Leicestershire & Rutland Fire Service	B4 Wood Market-Lutterworth-1968 B4 Gilmorton Rd-Lutterworth-1974 B4 Gilmorton Rd-Lutterworth-1981 **Conv to Chemical Incident Unit** C1/S30-Lancaster Place-Leicester-Leicestershire Fire Service KC40-LRFB
WRF971C		ET/FOT Salv/T	65	?	Staffordshire Fire Brigade	Reserve KC40-SFB
HNR600D		E/Salv	66	82	Leicestershire & Rutland Fire Service	Bridge St-Loughborough-1974 A1/N20 Epinal Way-Loughborough Leicestershire Fire Service KC40-LRFB

2598MV passed to the London FB in 1965, and was replaced by a Dennis F108 in 1972. This 1960 Commer QX served the old Middlesex County Fire Brigade at Heston. Today if you visited the station you would find 'state of the art technology' in the form of a Volvo FL6-14 Heavy Rescue Unit, keeping up the tradition of ET's at Heston.
Keith Wardell collection

GAJ421D		ET	66	78	North Riding of Yorkshire Fire Brigade	C1 East Rd-Northallerton-1969 C1 Crosby Rd-Northallerton-1974 E11 Crosbey Rd-Northallerton-1979 E1 Nth Marine Rd-Scarborough-1980 W6 Broughton Rd-Skipton-1982/North Yorkshire Fire Brigade KC40-Vernon-Davenport-**Yellow livery**
HBL642D		Foam/C	66	75	Berkshire & Reading Fire Brigade	B1 Caversham Rd-Reading-1974 W1 Caversham Rd-Reading-1975Royal Berkshire F & Rescue KC40-BRFB
KNR655E		E/SalvT	67	77	Leicestershire & Rutland Fire Service	Bull Head St-Wigston-1974 B1/S31 Bull Head St-Wigston-1977 Leicestershire Fire Service KC40-LRFB
KNR656E		E/SalvT	67	83	Leicestershire & Rutland Fire Service	Wood Market-Lutterworth-1968 Gilmorton Rd-Lutterworth-1974 B4/S37-Lutterworth-1976 B5/S38 Leicester Rd-Hinckley-1983/ Leicestershire F S KC40-LRFB
KNR657E		F/SalvT	67	83	Leicestershire & Rutland Fire Service	Bridge St-Loughborough-1974 A1/N20 Epinal Way-Loughborough Leicestershire FS KC40-LRFB
KNR658E		F/SalvT	67	83	Leicestershire & Rutland Fire Service	Broad Rd-Oakham-1974 D1/S33 Broad Rd-Oakham-1982-S33 South St-Oakham-1983 Leicestershire Fire Service KC 40-LRFB
PAN4E	CU.4 CIU.1	C/Unit	67	84	London Fire Brigade	G30 Harrow Rd-Wembley-1972 **Converted Chemical Incident Unit** Brigade Headquarters-Lambeth-1984 KC40-Strachan/Wadhams
PAN5E	CU.5	C/Unit	67	79	London Fire Brigade	H31 Old Town-Croyden-1972 Brigade Headquarters-Lambeth (Reserve)-1979 KC40-Strachan/Wadhams
PAN6E	CU.6	C/Unit	67	85	London Fire Brigade	F21Romford Rd-Stratford-1972 Brigade Headquarters-Lambeth-1985 KC40-Strachan/Wadhams
DRF590E		CAV	67	86	Staffordshire Fire Brigade	Lammascote Rd-Stafford KC40-SFB
ORX206F		Res/T	67	82	Berkshire & Reading Fire Brigade	B1 Caversham Rd-Reading-1974 W1 Caversham Rd-Reading-1982/Royal Berkshire F & Rescue KC40-BRFB
EJM203F		Res/T	67	87	Westmoreland County Fire Brigade	1 Busher Walk-Kendal-1974 E30 Busher Walk-Kendal-1987/Cumbria Fire Service KC40-Carmichael
KGS901G		ET	68	85	Perth & Kinross Fire Brigade (Scotland)	Dundas St-Comrie/Reserve-ET- KC40-HCB Angus
YRE894H		FOT Salv/T	69	80	Staffordshire Fire Brigade	Old Hednesford Rd-Cannock KC40-SFB
RCT500H		RRU	70	79	Kesteven County Fire Brigade	Skegness Fire Station-1974 /C1 Skegness-1978-Lincolnshire KC40 Air Van-LCFB
RDL940J		ET	70	80	Isle of White Fire Brigade	1 South St-Newport-1980 KC40-IoWFB

The Commer KC40 Walk-Thru van was the considered ideal chassis for the small specialist appliance used by many brigades in the 1960s and 70s. The Leicestershire & Rutland Fire Service operated six in many guises. This 1965 model, ENR200C, was originally based at Lutterworth as a Foam Tender but, in 1981, it was converted into a Chemical Incident Unit, painted red and transferred to Leicester Central where it was when photographed. *Michael Lawmon*

DTJ956J	89	Foam/C	71	79	Lancashire County Fire Brigade	E70 Broadway-Chadderton-1974 **Day-glo livery** C35 Broadway-Chadderton-1976 **Converted Hi-Expansion Foam Unit** A11 Bury New Rd-Broughton-1979 Greater Manchester CFS KC40-LCFB
LBW999L		ET	72	80	Oxfordshire Fire Service	A01 Cope Rd-Banbury KC40-Air Drive
BJV999L		ET	72	80	Grimsby County Borough Fire Brigade	#1 Peakes Lane-Grimsby-1974/C1 Peakes Lane-Grimsby-1975 **Converted to Control Unit** C1 Peakes Lane-Grimsby-1980/Humberside Fire Brigade KC40-Garner
TUD854L		ET	73	80	Oxfordshire Fire Service	A06 Sterling Rd-Kidlington KC40-Air Drive
HDE157N		ET	74	91	Pembrokeshire Fire Brigade (Wales)	Merlins Wall-Haverfordwest B1 Merlins Wall-Haverfordwest-1981 **Converted Foam/Salvage Tender** B1 Merlins Wall-Haverfordwest-1987 **Converted to Marine Rescue Unit** B2 Yorke St-Milford Haven-1991 KC40-PFB/DFB
GYM270N		Forced Entry/LU	74	?	London Fire Brigade	B21 High Rd-Clapham KC40-LFB
HA9241		C/Unit	75		Northern Ireland Fire Brigade	C02 Thomas St-Portadown KC50-Alexander
HA9242		C/Unit	75		Northern Ireland Fire Brigade	F10 Cliff Rd-Belleek KC-Alexander
IA2192		C/Unit	75		Northern Ireland Fire Brigade	E08 Church St-Kilrea KC50-Alexander
LEC729P		RLU	76	84	Cumbria Fire Service	Abbey Rd-Barrow in Furness KC40-CFS
REC839R		RLU	77	82	Cumbria Fire Service	King St-Workington KC40-CFS
REC840R		RLU	77	92	Cumbria Fire Service	Bridge Lane-Penrith-1985 /Reserve-1992 KC40-CFS
YEC462S		RLU	77	85	Cumbria Fire Service	Warwick St-Carlisle **Dodge KC40-CFS**
XRO912S		Foam/C	77	85	Buckinghamshire Fire Brigade	14 Sherwood Drive-Bletchley **Dodge KC40-BFB**
ELS631S		ET	77	83	Lothian & Borders Fire Brigade (Scotland)	Mcdonald Rd-Edingburgh **Dodge KC40-L&BFB**
YTS208T		RRU	78	94	Tayside Fire Brigade (Scotland)	A5 Garrison Rd-Montrose-1989/Reserve-**1994** **Dodge KC40-TFB**
YTS209T		RRU	78	89	Tayside Fire Brigade (Scotland)	A7 Academy St-Forfar- **Dodge KC40-TFB**
YTS210T		RRU	78	?	Tayside Fire Brigade (Scotland)	B8 High St-Kinross/Reserve-RRU-1994 **Dodge KC40-TFB**
YTS211T		RRU	78	?	Tayside Fire Brigade (Scotland)	B7 Atholl Rd-Pitlochry **Dodge KC40-TFB**
GEC487T		Foam/C	78	?	Cumbria Fire Service	Abbey Rd-Barrow in Furness **Dodge KC40-CFS**
FSX273T		ET	78	84	Lothian & Borders Fire Brigade (Scotland)	**Dodge KC40-L&BFB**
NPT502T		Water/RU	79	89	Durham County Fire Brigade	G Framwellgate Moor-Finchale Rd-Durham **Dodge KC40-DCFB**
CHB643V		Foam/C	80	?	Gwent Fire Brigade (Wales)	Station Hill-Abertillery **Dodge KC40-GFB**

As stated earlier, Leicestershire & Rutland operated several Commer KC40 Walk-Thru chassis for their specialist appliances. This Oakham - based Foam Unit, KNR658E, has the striking maroon livery used by that service for many years. The appliance was photographed shortly after passing to Leicestershire Fire Service ownership by when the 'Rutland' name has been removed.
Les Edkins

Types Superpoise Q Range V Range Forward- Control			Commer Chassied Specialist Appliances Weight 1-5 Tons up to 6 Tons up to 8 Tons 1500 cwt				The Commer range was used quite extensively after the war. The cab was similar to the one used on the Karrier range.
KAD765		FOT	50	67	Gloucestershire Fire Service		ex WRT Coleford-1965/20/A4 Severnside (Pilning)-1967 QX-Miles
PVK388		FOT	50	68	Newcastle & Gateshead Joint Fire Service		Operated from all of N&GFS stations QX-N&G JFS
PJV506		ET Salv/T	51	72	Grimsby County Borough Fire Brigade		#1 Alexandra Rd-Grimsby-1964 #1 Peakes Lane-Grimsby-1972 Superpoise-GFB
MUP418	064	FOT	51	76	Durham County Fire Brigade		ex WRT Ferryhill-1965/B16 Hedgeley Rd-Hebburn-1965 B16 Victoria Rd-Hebburn-1974/T Victoria Rd-Hebburn-1976 Tyne & Wear Metropolitan FB QX 21A-Miles
MUP419	065 12	FOT	51	69	Durham County Fire Brigade		ex WRT Consett-1965/C25 West Row-Stockton-1965 C25 South Rd Norton-1969-Teesside FB QX 21A-Miles
EBN706		Pump Salv/T	51	76	Bolton County Borough Fire Brigade		#1 Marsden Rd-Bolton-1967/#2 Crompton Way-Bolton-1974 B21 Crompton Way-Bolton-1976/Greater Manchester CFS QX 21A-Bellhouse & Harwell
FRX446		Heavy	52	72	Berkshire & Reading Fire Brigade		B1 Caversham Rd-Reading

		Rec/V					QX-Markhams
OKO197	262	Pump Salv/T	52	72	Kent Fire Brigade		43 Watling St-Medway QX 21A K1-HCB
OKO663	264	Pump Salv/T	52	65	Kent Fire Brigade		80 Upper Bridge St-Canterbury QX 21A K1-HCB
OKO664	265 P-265	Pump Salv/T	52	66	Kent Fire Brigade		4 South St-Bromley-1965 / H21-Bromley-1966-London FB QX 21A K1-HCB
OKM661	269	Pump Salv/T	52	69	Kent Fire Brigade		74 Grove Rd-Tunbridge Wells QX 21A K1-HCB
CKR304	273	Pump Salv/T	52	69	Kent Fire Brigade		17 Ladywell-Dover QX 21A K1-HCB
OKP938	274	Pump Salv/T	52	69	Kent Fire Brigade		19 Park Farm Rd-Folkestone QX 21A K1-HCB
OKP939	275	Pump Salv/T	52	72	Kent Fire Brigade		87 King St-Margate QX 21A K1-HCB
BYJ444		Pump Salv/T	52	?	Angus Area Fire Brigade (Scotland)		**QX-Carmichael**
OPT672	068	FOT	53	81	Durham County Fire Brigade		**ex WRT Washington-1969** A4/S4 Watling St-Bishop Auckland-1978/Reserve-1981 QX 21A-Miles
OPT673	069	FOT	53	81	Durham County Fire Brigade		ex WRT Seaham-1969 C21/D6 Surtees Rd-Peterlee-1977 /Reserve QX 21A-Miles
WMX234	HFT-3 HLL-1	HLL FOT	53	72	Middlesex Fire Brigade		35 The Burroughs-Hendon-1965 G24 The Burroughs-Hendon-1972 /London Fire Brigade QX-Waldergrave
WMX235	ST-4	Salv/T	53	65	Middlesex Fire Brigade		7 Coombes Croft-Tottenham-1965 QX Superpoise-MFB
PKE131	274	Pump Salv/T	53	72	Kent Fire Brigade		35 Wrotham Rd-Gravesend QX 21A K1-HCB
NVF237		FOT Salv/T	53	84	Norfolk Fire Service		**ex WRT B44 Fakenham-1969** B47 Kilhams Way-Kings Lynn-1984 QX-Carmichael
PKR56	384	HLL	53	70	Kent Fire Brigade		64 Pattenden Rd-Marden QX 42A-HCB
PKP857	363	FOT	53	71	Kent Fire Brigade		39 Whitegates-Gravesend Rd-Strood QX 42A-HCB
WMX235	ST-4	Salv/T	53	65	Middlesex Fire Brigade		7 Coombes Croft-Tottenham QX-Waldergrave
NRH117		Rec/V	54	?	City of Kingston upon Hull Fire Brigade		**ex WRT /** **?** QX-Cuerdon
RKM578	386	HLL	54	71	Kent Fire Brigade		39 Whitegates-Gravesend Rd-Strood QX 42A-HCB
RKM852	362	FOT	54	71	Kent Fire Brigade		80 Upper Bridge St-Canterbury QX 42A-HCB
RKM853	363	HLL	54	71	Kent Fire Brigade		19 Park Farm Rd-Folkestone QX 42A-HCB
RKR161	385	HLL	54	71	Kent Fire Brigade		80 Upper Bridge St-Canterbury QX 42A-HCB
13AMX	HL-4 HL-2	HLL	54	71	Middlesex Fire Brigade		65 London Rd-Heston-1965 D27 London Rd-Heston-1971 /London Fire Brigade QX-Waldergrave
15AMX	A7 CAV-2	CAV	54	69	Middlesex Fire Brigade		39 Harrow Rd-Wembley-1965 G30 Harrow Rd-Wembley-1969 /London Fire Brigade FC 1500 cwt-MFB
24CMX	HL-5	HLL	55	72	Middlesex Fire Brigade		31 Pinner Rd-Harrow-1965 G21 Pinner Rd-Harrow-1972/London Fire Brigade QX-Waldergrave
46CMX	HL-6	HLL	55	72	Middlesex Fire Brigade		4 Holtwhites Hill-Enfield

						J30 Carterhatch Lane-Enfield-1972 /London Fire Brigade QX-Waldergrave
NDG690		Pump Salv/T	55	69	Gloucestershire Fire Service	**ex WRT** / 11/12 Lansdowne Rd-Cheltenham-1960 11/12 Keynsham Rd-Cheltenham-1969 QX-Miles
NDG692		Pump Salv/T	55	69	Gloucestershire Fire Service	**ex WRT** / 15/07 Lainscroft Rd-Stroud-1964 15/07 Paganhill Lane-Stroud-1969 QX-Miles
TKJ573	**388 HL-9**	HLL	55	73	Kent Fire Brigade	Main Rd-Sidcup-1965 H23 Main Rd-Sidcup-1973 /London Fire Brigade QX 42A-HCB
TKJ574	**389**	HLL	55	71	Kent Fire Brigade	45 High St-Sittingbourne QX 42A-HCB
TKJ930	**380 FT-5**	FOT	55	71	Kent Fire Brigade	52 Erith Rd-Erith-1965 E27 Erith Rd-Erith-1971 /London Fire Brigade QX 42A-HCB
52CMX	**HL-7 HL-7F**	HLL	56	72	Middlesex Fire Brigade	71 Church Rd-Hayes D30 Shepistone Lane-Hayes-1972/London Fire Brigade QX-Waldergrave
TAU999		C/Unit	56	76	City of Nottingham	#1 Shakespeare St-Central-1974 B18 Shakespeare St-Central-1976/Nottinghamshire FB Q2-Superpoise-NFB
RYX400		HLL	56	79	Worcester City & County Fire Brigade	E27 Birmingham Rd-Redditch-1974 27 Birmingham Rd-Redditch-1979 /Hereford & Worcester FB ; Q4-Superpoise-HOS
SXF521		HLL	57	?	West Riding of Yorkshire	B16 Knottingley Fire Station QX-Superpoise-HOS
999BTV		Foam Salv/T	59	?	City of Nottingham	Shakespeare St-Nottingham QX-City Engineers Dept
238COG	**23**	C/Unit	60	79	City of Birmingham	1 Lancaster Circus-Central-1974 A1 Lancaster Circus-Central-1979/West Midlands Fire Service ; FC 1500 cwt-Lomas

One of only two local authority Recovery Vehicles built on the Commer QX chassis, FRX446 was delivered in 1952 to the Caversham Rd station in Reading from where it went on to give 20 years service. These machines were the first Heavy Rescue Vehicles built and this machine was replaced by a vehicle with a crane, this time on a Dodge K Series chassis. *Keith Wardell collection*

Reg	Code	Type			Brigade	Notes
1019MX	FT-1 FT-7	FOT	61	77	Middlesex Fire Brigade	62 Gunnersbury Lane-Acton-1965 D22 Gunnersbury Lane-Acton-1977/London Fire Brigade QX-Waldergrave
380GEO		FOT	62	88	Cumberland County Fire Brigade	**ex WRT Keswick-1976**/Hensingham-Whitehaven-1988 Cumbria Fire Service QX-Carmichael-CFS
PCM662	1045	FOT	63	92	Birkenhead County Fire Brigade	Whetstone Lane-Birkenhead-1974 W1 Exmouth St-Birkenhead-1981 **Converted Marine & Ship Unit** C1 Studholme St-Bankhall-1992/Merseyside Fire Brigade VAC-Sun-MFB
192MRM		FOT	64	88	Cumberland County Fire Brigade	**ex WRT Whitehaven/Millom-1979** Warwick St-Carlisle-1988/Cumbria Fire Service QX-Carmichael-CFS
CEM684		FOT	65	76	Bootle County Borough Fire Brigade	Strand Rd-Bootle-1974 C5/6 Strand Rd-Bootle-1976/Merseyside Fire Brigade VAC-BCFB
DAD257C		FOT	65	65	Gloucestershire Fire Service	20/A4 Severnside (Pilning)-**Written off in RTA** **Pyrene foam equipment transfered to Ford -KDF832E** VAC-Dennis M/Pyrene
CHO693C		C/Unit	65	77	Hampshire Fire Service	**ex Civil Defenece** / C30 North Walls-Winchester FC 1500 cwt-HFS
FKE104C	370	Pump Salv/T	65	?	Kent Fire Brigade	80 Upper Bridge St-Canterbury V AC K2-HCB
OKN831G	399	C/Unit	68	?	Kent Fire Brigade	HQ The Godlands-Maidstone FC 1500 cwt-KFB
MSA83G		FOT Salv/T	69	86	North Eastern Area Fire Brigade (Scotland)	King St-Aberdeen-1975 S96 King St-Aberdeen-1986/Grampian Fire Brigade VCKW-HCB Angus
AMC157H		WRC	70	80	East Sussex Fire Brigade	B17 Beacon Rd-Crowborough VAC TS3-ESFB

Middlesex Fire Brigade operated 1091MX, a 1961 Foam Tender as part of a large fleet of Commer specialist appliances. Bodied by Waldergrave the appliance served out of Gunnersbury Lane fire station in Acton for many years, passing to London Fire Brigade in 1965, where it is seen at D27 Heston while operating as a reserve in the livery of the London Fire Brigade.
The late Alan Batchelor

DENNIS

Reg No	Fleet No NFS-Magirus Ladder No MG	TYPE	YR	OS	Appliance & Brigade Name Dennis Lancet Turntable Ladders	Details/Stations The earlier TL's were mounted on the G type chassis, with later models being mounted on the 8 Ton Lancet chassis. The G Type was powered by a 4 cylinder petrol engine, with the later having the 9.5 litre Meadows petrol engine.
						John Morris of Salford were the Magirus dealers for over 50 years
?		TL	21	?	Cromer Fire Brigade (Norfolk)	? / Converted in 1935 Morris-Magirus 85 L Wooden
?		TL	22	?	Glasgow Fire Service (Scotland)	? / Sold to Ayr-1930 Morris-Magirus-85 L Wooden
GB1887	MG-1	TL	22	?	Glasgow Fire Service (Scotland)	St Georges Fire Station Morris-Magirus-85 L Wooden
?		TL	23	42	Brighton County Borough FB	Preston Circus-Brighton Morris-Magirus-85'L-Wooden
BA4303	MG-2	TL	23	42	City of Salford	The Crescent-Salford Morris-Magirus-85'L-Wooden
EB2713 OL 34 ?	MG-3	TL	23	47	Wisbech Fire Brigade (Cambridgeshire)	Horse Fair-Wisbech Morris-Magirus-85'L-Wooden
GB7187	MG-4	TL	24	46	Glasgow Fire Service (Scotland)	Partick Fire Station Morris-Magirus-85 L Wooden
?		TL	24	?	West Ham County Borough FB	? Morris-Magirus 85 L Wooden
WU2113	MG-5	TL	25	47	Harrogate Fire Brigade	Albert St-Harrogate Morris-Magirus-85'L-Wooden
?		TL	25	?	Scunthorpe Fire Brigade	Scunthorpe Fire Station Morris-Magirus 85 L Wooden
XS1554	MG-6	TL	26	43	Paisley Fire Brigade (Scotland)	Paisley Fire Station Ayr Fire Station Morris-Magirus-85 L Wooden
UH1740	MG-7	TL	26	42	Cardiff City Fire Brigade (Wales)	Westgate St-Cardiff Morris-Magirus-85'L-Wooden
TR3863	MG-8	TL	27	43	City of Southampton	Portsmouth Rd-Woolston-Southampton-1940 Wimborne Rd-Poole-Dorset FB-1943 Morris-Magirus-80'L-Wooden
WE 407	MG-9	TL	27	47	City of Sheffield	West Bar Fire Station Morris-Magirus 90 L Wooden
?	TL7	TL	28	38 ?	LCC London Fire Brigade	? Morris-Magirus 85 L Wooden
?	TL8	TL	28	38 ?	LCC London Fire Brigade	? Morris-Magirus 85 L Wooden
?	TL9	TL	29	38 ?	LCC London Fire Brigade	? Morris-Magirus 85 L Wooden
AN8434	MG-10	TLP	28	47	West Ham County Borough FB	Stratford Fire Station Morris-Magirus-85'-Wooden-400gpmP
EM2183	MG-11	TL	28	45	Bootle County Borough FB	Strand Rd-Bootle Morris-Magirus-85'L-Wooden
HJ8300	MG-12	TL	28	47	Southend County Borough FB	London Rd-Southend Morris-Magirus-85 L Wooden
BR8023	MG-13	TL	29	45	Sunderland County Borough	Dun Cow St-Sunderland-1942 Station Rd-Fulwell-Sunderland-1950 Morris-Magirus-85'L-Wooden

GG 482	MG-14	TL	30	46	Glasgow Fire Service (Scotland)	Govan Fire Station-Glasgow Morris-Magirus-85 L-Wooden
JA1345	MG-15	TL	30	?	Stockport County Borough FB	#1 Whitehill St-Stockport Morris-Magirus-85 L-Wooden
GT6693	TL11 MG-16	TL	31	47	LCC London Fire Brigade	F1 Southwark Bridge Rd-Southwark Morris-Magirus-85 L-Wooden
GT6692	TL10 MG-17	TL	31	43	LCC London Fire Brigade	**ex London Fire Brigade -1938** Northgate St-City of Chester FB-1943 Morris-Magirus-85'L-Wooden
UN5623	MG-18	TL	31	52	Colwyn Bay FB (Wales)	Abergale Rd-Colwyn Bay - ? Denbigh & Montogomery Morris-Magirus85'L-Wooden
GT6694	TL12 MG-19	TL	32	60	LCC London Fire Brigade	B32 Brunswick Rd-1954/Reserve-1960 **Ladder re-chassied onto AEC-Mercury VYE234-TL34** Morris -Magirus-100'L
CZ 503	MG-20	TL	32	?	Belfast Fire Brigade	**Belfast Fire Station's-?** Morris-Magirus-100 L
ALW478	TL13 MG-21	TL	34	62	LCC London Fire Brigade	D69 Tooting-1958/Reserve-1962 **Preserved** Morris-Magirus-100'L
ALW479	TL14 MG-22	TL	34	62	LCC London Fire Brigade	C40 New Cross-1954/Reserve-1962 **Preserved** Morris-Magirus-100'L
ALW480	TL15 MG-23	TL	34	62	LCC London Fire Brigade	B32 Bishopsgate-1959/Reserve-1962 Morris-Magirus-100'L
BLC555	TL16 MG-24	TL	35	62	LCC London Fire Brigade	D63-Dockhead-1954/C40-New Cross-1962 **Preserved** Morris-Magirus-100'L
BYV321	TL17 MG-25	TL	36	65	LCC London Fire Brigade	A1 Manchester Square-1962/Reserve-1965 **Sold to AWE Aldermaston-1965-66** Morris-Magirus-100'L
BYV322	TL18 MG-26	TL	36	67	LCC London Fire Brigade	A10 Kensington-1965/Reserve-1967 Morris-Magirus-100'L
BYV323	TL19	TL	36	40	LCC London Fire Brigade	**Destroyed in an air raid during the Blitz-1940**
JX3942	MG-27	TLP	36	59	Halifax County Borough FB	Skircoat Moor Rd-Halifax Morris-Magirus 100'L

This picture shows the only cabbed version of the Dennis Merryweather Turntable Ladder combination. This appliance LMC768 served out of the Harrow Road station of the old Wembley Fire Brigade for 21 years before it passed to the ownership of the Middlesex Fire Brigade in 1947. The machine was fitted with an in built 600gpm pump. It is believed the ladders were later rechassied onto a AEC Mercury chassis, though details are very sketchy.
Roy Goodey

DGJ311	TL20 MG-28	TLP	37	67	LCC London Fire Brigade	D66 Brixton-1954/D63-Dockhead- 1959/Reserve-1967 **TL-2 London FB-700gpmP** Morris-Magirus-100'L
AYS524	MG-29	TLP	37	66	Glasgow Fire Service (Scotland)	Fire Station Unknown Morris-Magirus 100'L-**500gpmP**
ELL121	TL23 MG-30	TLP	38	67	LCC London Fire Brigade	B35 Cannon St-1964/Reserve-1967 **Damaged at Eldon St Fire-118 Pump-8 Turntable Ladders/Railway Warehouse Fire which cost the lives of 3 Firemen when a wall collapsed-21/12/1951 Repaired and returned to duty-Preserved** Morris-Magirus-100'L-**700gpmP**
ELL122	TL24 MG-31	TLP	38	65	LCC London Fire Brigade	A13 Edgware Rd-1960 /G25 West Hampstead-1965 Morris-Magirus-100'L-**700gpmP**
EHN118	MG-32	TLP	38	59	Darlington County Borough FB	Borough Rd-Darlington Morris-Magirus-100'L-**500gpmP**
HME593	TL2 MG-33	TL	38	62	Harrow & Wealdstone Fire Brigade	Pinner Rd-Harrow-1948/B30 Harrow-Middlesex F&AS-1962 Morris-Magirus-85'L-**600gpmP**

RC6226	MW No MW-27	TLP	38	58	Derby County Borough FB	**Merryweather Ladder No** D1 Jury St-Derby CBFB-1963 **MWL-27 was re-chassied onto GGK941** Merryweather 100'L-**350gpmP**
ELL123	TL25 MW-28	TLP	38	65	LCC London Fire Brigade	A6-Greycoat Place-Westminster-London-1964/Reserve-1965 Merryweather-100'L-**700gpmP**
LMC768	TLP5 MW-32	TLP	40	61	Middlesex Fire Brigade (Ambulance Service)	B39-Harrow Rd- Wembley **Enclosed Cab Version Ladders re-chassied onto AEC Mercury-2600MV ?** Merryweather-100'L-**600gpmP**
GGK941 NFS order	TL28 MW-34	TL	40	64	LCC London Fire Brigade	B28 Brunswick Rd-London-1947 Division St-Sheffield-City of Sheffield FB-1958 **Ladders Rechassied of f RC6226-Derby County Borough** D1 Jury St-Derby-1964 Merryweather-100'L
CTO10 NFS order	MW-35	TL	40	65	City of Nottingham	Shakespeare St-Nottingham-1955 /Abbey Rd-Dunkirk-1965 Merryweather-100'L
GGK943 NFS order	TL29 MW-36	TL	40	65	LCC London Fire Brigade	B23 Kingsland Rd-London FB-1965 C30 Hornsey Rd-Holloway-1967 Merryweather-100'L
GGK944 NFS order	TL30 MW-37	TL	40	66	LCC London Fire Brigade	C43 Woolwich Rd-East Greenwich-1962 Merryweather-100'L
GGK945 NFS order	TL31 MW-38	TL	40	67	LCC London Fire Brigade	Headquarters/Training Centre Southwark **Transferred to Eastbourne County Borough-1949** Merryweather-100'L
GGK946 NFS order	TL32 MW-39	TL	40	65	LCC London Fire Brigade	A4 Euston Rd-Euston-London FB-1965/ Reserve **GLC TL No-3/Preserved in Wisconsin-USA** Merryweather-100'L
GGK947 NFS order	TL33 MW-40	TL	40	51	LCC London Fire Brigade	C49 Lea Green-London FB-1951/**Damaged at Eldon St-Railway Warehouse Fire-21/11/51-Fireman at head of ladder had lucky escape when the wall collapsed. It was at an extended height of 55' and whilst descending it was hit and caused sudden descent of 12'. The fireman sustained a dislocated shoulder.** Merryweather-100'L
GGK948 NFS order	TL34 MW-41	TL	40	63	LCC London Fire Brigade	High St-Leytonstone-1947 Rainsford Ave-Chelmsford-Essex County FB-1963 Merryweather-100'L
DCR473 NFS order	MW-42	TL	40	68	City of Southampton	D54-St Mary's Rd-Southampton-1958 D56-Woolston-Southampton-1968 Merryweather-100'L

GCD802 NFS order	TL1 MW-50	TL	41	59	Brighton County Fire Brigade	Preston Circus-Brighton-1957 /Reserve-1959 **Discovered in scrap yard in Sussex** Merryweather-100'L
CBK807 NFS order	TL8 MW-51	TL	41	73	City of Portsmouth	Somers Rd-City of Portsmouth-1963 Res-1973-**Preserved** Merryweather-100'L
LME418 NFS order	TL7 MW-52	TL	41	60	Middlesex Fire Brigade (Ambulance Service)	A07 The Green-Tottenham **Ladders re-chassied onto AEC Mercury-2600MV ?** Merryweather-100'L
FVP605 NFS order	50 MW-53	TL	41	65	City of Birmingham	A1 Lancaster Circus-Birmingham-1965 **This appliance was involved in an RTA where it ended up embedded in a house. Repaired and returned to duty.** Merryweather-100'L
DRY198 NFS order	10 MW-54	TL	41	62	Leicester City Fire Brigade	A1 Lancaster Place-Leicester/**Preserved** Merryweather-100'L
CKG184 NFS order	MW-55	TL	41	55	Cardiff City Fire Brigade (Wales)	Westgate St-Cardiff-1944 D63 Windermere Rd-Leigh -Lancashire CFB1955 Merryweather-100'L
AJD324 NFS order	MW-64	TL	41	60	West Ham County Borough FB	Silvertown Fire Station/Romford Rd-Stratford-1960 **Ladders Re-chassied onto AEC Mercury-TAN149** Merryweather-100'L
GGK949 NFS order	TL35 MW-65	TL	41	74	LCC London Fire Brigade	A08 Tottenham Lane-Hornsey-1954/ Ascroft St-Oldham-Oldham County BFB-1974 Merryweather-100'L
CDR287 NFS order	MW-66	TL	41	64	City of Plymouth	Crownhill Rd-Plymouth Merryweather-100'L
GLW404 NFS order	MW-67	TL	41	**63 ?**	City of Stoke on Trent	Longton Fire Station-Stoke-1954 High Street-Burton upon Trent-Burton CB-1963 Merryweather-100 L
GLW409 NFS order	MW-74	TL	42	63	City of Manchester	**Originally going to Singapore-Cancelled due to the war.** London Rd-Manchester Whitehill St-Stockport-Stockport CB Merryweather -100 L

This Dennis 100ft Merryweather Turntable Ladder GXA82 served at the Ladymead station in Guilford. The Surrey Fire Brigade was lucky to get one of a batch delivered to the NFS in 1943, and this would serve the town for over 21 years. The appliance would have been a nightmare for any new recruits who had no experience of polishing! They would probably have preferred it in the war livery when all brass and chrome was painted NFS grey.
Keith Wardell collection

?		TL	42	?	**Royal Navy**	**Chatham Dockyard-Royal Navy-Kent** Merryweather 100 L
GLW424 NFS order	MW-89	TL	42	68	City of Bristol	Bedminster-Bristol -1952/ **Period at Yeovil/Somerset ?** Speedwell Rd-Speedwell-Bristol-1968 Merryweather-100'L
GLW435 NFS order	MW-99	TL	42	62	City of Oxford	Rewley Rd-Oxford Merryweather-100'L
GLW436 NFS order	MW-100	TL	42	65	Huntingdonshire & Peterborough FB	Swindon-Wiltshire FB-1945/ **Leicester City FB ?** Dogsthorpe Rd-Peterborough- 1968/ **Preserved-1988** Merryweather-100'L
GLW432 NFS order	MW-101	TL	42	64	Carlisle Fire Brigade	**Originally ordered for Leyton** /Warwick St-Carlisle-1964 Merryweather-85'L
GLW433 NFS order	MW-102	TL	42	62	? (Wales)	**Originally ordered for Walthamstowe / Cardiff Area-?** Coast Rd-Rhyl-Flintshire FB-1945 A1-St Anne's St-City of Chester FB-1962 Merryweather-85'L
GLW434 NFS order	MW-98	TL	42	67	Fife Fire Brigade (Scotland)	Carnegie Drive-Dunfermline-1948 Dunnikeir Rd-Kirkaldy -1967 Merryweather-100'L
GXA78 NFS order	MW-127	TL	43	59	Kent Fire Brigade	D Div-Cavendish St- Ramsgate-Kent **Sold to Rentokil Oxford in 1962** Merryweather-100'L
GXA81 NFS order	MW-129	TL	43	67	City of Plymouth	Camels Head-Plymouth 1948 Royal Leamington Spa-1967-Warwick CFB/**Preserved-1984** Merryweather-100'L
GXA82 NFS order	MW-128	TLP	43	64	Surrey County Council Fire Brigade	Ladymead-Guilford-1961 / High St-Esher-1964 Merryweather-100'L
GXA84 NFS order	MW-130	TL	43	61	Berkshire & Reading Fire Brigade	Mckenzie St-Slough-1955 / Tuns Lane-Slough-1961 Merryweather-100'L
GXA87 NFS order	MW-131	TL	43	60	South Western Area Fire Brigade (Scotland)	Kilmarnock Fire Station Merryweather-100'L
GXA89 NFS order	MW-133	TL	43	63	Bedfordshire Fire Brigade	01-Barkers Lane-Bedford-1948 00 Studley Rd-Luton-Luton CBFB-1963 Merryweather-100'L
GXA91 NFS order	MW-134	TL	43	60	Bootle Fire Brigade	Strand Rd-Bootle-1960/**Preserved** **Merryweather-100'L**
GXA92 NFS order	MW-135	TL	43	68	City of Coventry	Hales St-Coventry-1946/Stechford-City of Birmingham-1956 Peakes Lane-Grimsby CBFB-1968 Merryweather-100'L
GXA93 NFS order	MW-136	TL	43	62	Kent Fire Brigade	D Div-Market Place-Deal-Kent-1946/ DD King St-Margate Merryweather-100'L
GXA94 NFS order	MW-137	TL	43	68	Burnley County Borough FB	E90 Manchester Rd-Burnley-1955 B37-South Shore-Blackpool CBFB-1968 Merryweather-100'L
GXA95 NFS order	MW-138	TLP	43	74	West Riding of Yorkshire Fire Brigade	Goole Fire Station-1951-Keighley Fire Station-1969 **Peakes Lane Grimsby-Grimsby CBFB- 1974 ?**
GXA96 NFS order	MW-139	TLP	43	65	Leeds City (West Yorkshire)	Gipton-City of Leeds FB-1947-Albert St-Harrogate-1951 Stansfield Rd-Todmorden-1965 West Riding of Yorkshire Fire Brigade
GXA97 NFS order	MW-140	TL	42	68	Fife Fire Brigade (Scotland)	Dunnikeir Rd-Kirkaldy-Fife-1968 Merryweather-100'L
GXA98 NFS order	MW-141	TL	43	?	Glasgow Fire Service (Scotland)	Glasgow Fire Service-Station Unkown- **Preserved Glasgow Transport Museum**
GXA99 NFS order	MW-142	TL	43	58	Burton on Trent (Staffordshire)	Burton on Trent Fire Station-1946/ 5 Moseley Rd-Birmingham-1958 **Preserved** Merryweather-100'L
GXA100 NFS order	MW-143	TL	43	63	Cambridge	**Cambridge Area - ?** / A2 Cowdrey Ave-Colchester Essex Merryweather-100'L

Chassis		F14 F7 F17-21			Dennis F7 & 14 & 17 & 21 Chassied Turntable Ladders	
Chassis		F14 F7 F17-21			Wheelbase 13 ft 6 in 13 ft 6 in 16 ft 3 in	The chassis on the F14 had a wheel base of 13ft 6in . It proved an ideal base for the Magirus and Metz ladders. They were normally fitted with the Rolls Royce B81petrol engine. Some were also fitted with the Dennis No2 pump.
GSA999		TL	50	78	North Eastern Fire Brigade (Scotland)	King St-Aberdeen-NE FB **Ladder removed from Leyland Lynx RG1066-1928** Ladder removed in 1955 and scrapped. **Re-built as Pump/E Sold to British Aluminium-Now Preserved** F7-Dennis- Metz-Wooden-85'L
LCE212		TL	53	79	Cambridgeshire Fire & Rescue Service	S Div B01 Parkside-Cambridge. **Sold to Lagos, Algarve-Portugal** F14-Dennis-Metz-104
GHE218		TL	54	72	Barnsley County Borough Fire Brigade	A Div Broadway-Barnsley F14-Dennis-Metz-100'L
UEH373		TL	54	76	City of Stoke on Trent	Hanley-CoST FB-1968/Uttoxeter Rd-Longton-1974 N Div Uttoxeter Rd-Longton-1976 Staffordshire FB/**Preserved in Merseyside Museum** F17-Dennis-Metz-104'L
XEV978		TL	54	71	Essex County Fire Brigade	Rainham Rd-Dagenham-1965 L25 Rainham Rd-Dagenham-1966/Reserve-1971 London Fire Brigade-**Sold to Rentokil's** F14-Dennis-Metz- 104'L
MGB853		TL	54	77?	Glasgow Fire Service (Scotland)	A1 Ingram St-Central-1967/C3 Partick-Glasgow-1975 Strathclyde Fire Brigade; F14-Dennis -Metz-100'L
EJV955		TLP	54	90	Grimsby County Borough FB	#1 Alexandra Rd-Grimsby-1964 #1 Peakes Lane-Grimsby-1974/C1-Grimsby-1990 Humberside FB-**Preserved** F17-Dennis-Metz-100'L
RKB300	E-9	TLP	54	70	City of Liverpool	#1 Hatton Gardens-Liverpool-1968 Training School-1970 F21-Dennis-Metz-100'L
OZ9607		TLP	54	?	Belfast Fire Brigade (Northern Ireland)	Central Fire Station-Belfast/**Started life with 125'L , shortened to 100' Bears scares of the civil unrest of the 1970's.Also has armoured glass. Preserved** F17-Dennis-Metz-100'L
YRI584		TLP	54	76	Dublin Fire Brigade (Irish Republic)	Dublin Central Fire Station /Preserved F17-Dennis-Metz-100'L
LSA9		TL	55	82	North Eastern Area Fire Brigade (Scotland)	King St-Aberdeen-1974 / S Div 96 King St-Aberdeen-1982 Grampian FB / **Preserved** F14-Dennis-Metz-100'L
YAU999		TL	55	78	City of Nottingham	Shakespeare St-Central-1965 /Abbey Rd-Dunkirk-1974 B21 Dunkirk-1978 Nottinghamshire FB/**Preserved** F21-Dennis-Metz-100'L
TUA604		TLP	57	76	Leeds City Fire Brigade	Park Street-Leeds Central-City of Leeds FB-1974 D11 Kirkstall Rd-Leeds Central-West Yorkshire FB-1976 F14-Dennis- Metz-100'L
PNN999		TL	57	72	Nottinghamshire County Council Fire Brigade	Rosemary St-Mansfield-1972/**Preserved** F14-Dennis-Metz-100'L
SKV899		TL	56	76	City of Coventry	2 Sir Henry Parkes Rd-Canley-1974 C02 Sir Henry Parkes Rd-Canley-1975 / West Midlands FS F17-Dennis-Metz- 100'L
PDK717		TL	57	79	City of Rochdale	Maclure Rd-Rochdale CBFB-1974 / C30-Rochdale-1975 Greater Manchester FS/Reserve-1979 **Preserved** F21-Dennis-Metz-125'L
CJP800		TL	57	76	Wigan County Borough FB	Chapel Lane-Wigan CBFB-1963 / Robin Park Rd--1974 B24 Robin Park Rd-Wigan-1976 Greater Manchester FS F21-Dennis-Metz-100'L

					Dennis F27 Chassied Turntable Ladders	This chassis was fitted with the Rolls Royce B81 Petrol Engine.
UCD999	2	TL	57	84	Brighton County Borough FB	A4 Preston Circus-1967/Roedean Rd-Rottingdean-1974 A5 Roedean Rd-Rottingdean-1984 East Sussex FB/**Preserved** Dennis-Metz-104'L
SUS149		TL	57	60	Glasgow Fire Service (Scotland)	This appliance may have been a F14 model. South-B1 Glasgow FS **This TL was destroyed in the explosion and fire at the Whisky Bond Warehouse in Cheapside, Glasgow. 19 Firemen /Salvage Corps personnel were killed.** Dennis-Metz-100'L
WCR213	No-9	TLP	58	76	City of Southampton	St Marys Rd-Southampton-1974 D54 St Marys Rd-Southampton-1975 Reserve/Hampshire FB Dennis-Magirus-100'L
WKV986	TL-3	TLP	58	80	City of Coventry	1 Hales St-Coventry-1964/3 Foleshill Rd-Foleshill-1974 B05-Foleshill-1976 B6-Binley-1979/Reserve-1980 /West Midlands FS Dennis-Metz-100'L
250AUP	192 11	TL	58	76	Durham County Fire Brigade	West Row-Stockton-1965-Durham County FB South Rd-Norton-Teesside FB-1974 South Rd-N2-Norton-Cleveland County FB-1976 **Loaned to Kent Fire Brigade Sold Humberside FB-Calvert Rd-Hull West-1980** Dennis-Metz-100'L
RSA193		TL	58	86	North Eastern Area Fire Brigade (Scotland)	North Anderson Drive-Aberdeen-1974 E77 North Anderson Drive-Aberdeen-Grampian FB-1984/Reserve-1986**Preserved** Dennis-Metz-100'L
49WPA		TL	61	79	Surrey County Council Fire Brigade	High St-Epsom-1976 /Reserve-1979 Haydon-Magirus-100'L
221VPB		TL	61	79	Surrey County Council Fire Brigade	Addelstone Moor-Weybridge-Chertsey -1979 Haydon-Magirus-100'L

PDK717, a superbly restored Dennis F21 with a 125' Metz ladder, looks as good today as it was when delivered in 1957. It is currently stored at the Maclure Road fire station in Rochdale where it served for 22 years. Later in its career it had the cab painted white, but when displayed at the FSPG Chacewater Rally in 1993, it was in its original livery.
Clive Shearman

420ABK	9	TL	62	75	City of Portsmouth	#2 Copner Rd-Copner-1974 B20 Copner Rd-1975/Hampshire Fire Brigade Dennis-Metz-100'L
TVG999		TL	62	82	City of Norwich	Bethel St-Norwich-1974 Bethel St-Norwich-Norfolk FS-1982 **Loaned to Cambridgeshire F&RS-B01 Cambridge-1984** **Preserved** Haydon-Magirus-100'L
700EJF	TL-9	TL	62	84	Leicester City Fire Brigade	#1 Lancaster Place-Central- 1974 SD30 Lancaster Place-Central- Leicestershire FS-1984 **Preserved** Haydon-Magirus-100'L
4000ED		TL	62	81	Warrington County Borough FB	Heathside-Warrington CBFB-1968 Winwick St-Warrington CBFB-1974 B1 Winwick St-Warrington-1981 Cheshire FB**/Preserved** Haydon-Magirus-100'L
5341UP	190	TL	63	85	Durham County Fire Brigade	Finchale Rd-Framwell Gate Moor- Durham-1985 **Sold to Kent Fire Brigade -Last seen derelict in Kent** Dennis-Magirus-100'L

The City of Leicester Dennis F27 Turntable Ladder 700EJF out of their Lancaster Place station for over 20 years. Most Magirus ladders had bodywork by David Haydon who had his premisis in the old Lyngard Street station in Birmingham. The machine carries the fleet number 9 seen in the photograph, which also shows its replacement which was A131KAY, an Iveco Magirus DLK23 delivered in 1984. *David Thomas*

The City of Norwich operated TVG999, a Dennis F27 with Haydon/Magirus 100' Turntable Ladder, from their Bethel Street station in Norwich, for nearly 20 years. It then deputised at Cambridge when their Shelvoke & Drewry/Metz ladder was unavailable following a road accident. *Michael Lawmon*

					Dennis F37 & 107 Chassied Turntable Ladders	The chassis was offered with either a Rolls Royce B80/B61 Petrol or Perkins T6.354 Diesel engine.
8118HA	2	TL	63	79	Smethwick &West Bromwich Joint Fire Brigade	Hargate Lane-West Bromwich-1974 D08 Hargate Lane-West Bromwich- West Midlands FS-1979 F107- Haydon-Magirus-100'L
CPF210B		TL	64	80	Surrey County Council Fire Brigade	Church St-Epsom-1965 Addelstone Moor-Weybridge-Chertsey-1980 F37-Haydon-Magirus-100'L
APA229B		TL	64	82	Surrey County Council Fire Brigade	By Pass, Ladymead Guilford-1979/Reserve-1982 F37-Haydon-Magirus-100'L
CDU293B		TL	64	79	City of Coventry	1 Hales St-Coventry-1974/C01 Hales St-Coventry-1976 A01 Lancaster Circus-Central-1978 /West Midlands FS F37-Haydon -Magirus-100'L
ABU736B		TL	64	82	Oldham County Borough FB	Ascroft St-Oldham CB-1974 / C33 Ascroft St-Oldham-1975 C30 Maclure Rd-Rochdale-1982 Greater Manchester FS F37-Haydon-Magirus-100'L
BEN99C		TL	65	80	Bury County Borough FB	The Rock-Bury CBFB-1974 C36 Bury-Greater Manchesterter-1980 F107-Haydon-Magirus-100'L
BEO864C		TL	65	82	Barrow in Furrness County Borough FB	Abbey Rd-Barrow-1974 / B Div-Barrow-1982 Cumbria FS **Ladders Re-ch onto Dodge G16C-SHH26X-Cumbria FS** F37-Haydon-Brade & Leigh Magius-100'L
GDW156D		TL	66	82	Newport County Borough FS (Wales)	01 Malpas Rd-Newport CBFS-1974 B11 Archibald St-Maindee-1982 / Gwent Fire Brigade F37-Dennis-Metz-100'L
MHA599F	141	TL	67	85	Smethwick & West Bromwich Joint Fire Brigade	E06 Oldbury-Smethwick CBFB-1974 D01 Old Park Lane-Oldbury-1980 Reserve-1985 West Midlands FS F107-Carmichael-Magirus-100'L

					Dennis F 123 & 125 DF133 Series Turntable Ladders	
NTN876R (later RTN144S)		TL	77	91	Tyne & Wear Metropolitan FB	V Dryden Rd-Gateshead-1984 D Pilgrim St-Newcastle Central-1989/Res-1991 / **Preserved** F123-Carmichael-Magirus-100'L
VCU581T		TL	78	95	Tyne & Wear Metropolitan FB	N Dun Cow St-Sunderland-1988 Reserve-Date F123-Carmichael-Magirus-100'L
VSG999V		TL	80	83	Fife Fire Brigade (Scotland)	A1 Carnegie Road, Dunfermline - **withdrawn** F123-Dennis-Merryweather-**XRL30** 100'L
MWX201V		TL	80	91	West Yorkshire Fire Service	A11 Nelson St-Bradford-1991 **Ladder Re-chassied off AEC Mercury-PKU833** **Sold to Access Stone Cleaning Ltd-Huddersfield** F125-G&T Power-Merryweather-100'L
KKE821V		TL	80	92	Kent Fire Brigade	ND 35 Coldharbour Rd-Northfleet-Thameside-1992 **Re-chassied ladder off Commer Maguirs 113LKE ?** F125-Carmichael-Magirus-100'L
RVW852W		TL	81	90	Essex County Fire Brigade	B27 Broadmayne-Basildon-1986 Reserve-1990 **Re-chassied Ladder off AEC Mercury-XJN618** F125-G&T Power-Merryweather-100'L
MKE886W	182	TL	81		Kent Fire Brigade	SD 60 Maidstone- F125-Carmichael-Magirus DL30U
MKE887W	183	TL	81	94	Kent Fire Brigade	DD 89 Margate Rd-Thanet-1994 F125-Carmichael-Magirus-DL30U
MKE888W	184	TL	81		Kent Fire Brigade	SD 19 Park Farm Rd-Folkestone F125-Carmichael-Magirus-DL30U
JDC296W	8	TL	81	94	Cleveland County Fire Brigade	S4 Trunk Rd-Redcar-1994 **Ladder Re-chassied off AEC Mercury-OXG950** F125-G&T Power-Merryweather-100'L

KKY940W		TL	81		South Yorkshire County Fire Service	ED 6 Ledger Way-Doncaster F127-Dennis-Magirus DL30U
PHL331X		TL	82		South Yorkshire County Fire Service	ED 18 Fitzwilliam Rd-Rotherham F127-Dennis-Magirus DL30U
ACM390X	1199	TL	82	94	Merseyside Metropolitan FB	S1 Mather Ave-Liverpool-1991 /Reserve-1994 **Ladder Re-chassied off AEC Mercury-?** F125-Dennis-Merryweather-100'L
ACM404X	1201	TL	82	92	Merseyside Metropolitan FB	C3 Canning Place-Liverpool-1989 Reserve-1991 **Ladder Re-chassied off AEC Mercury-?** F125-Dennis-Merryweather-100'L
CWY157Y	183	TL	82	**95**	West Yorkshire Fire Service	**ex CD Outcote Bank-Huddersfield- 1986**/ Reserve-1995 **Sold to Kent Fire Brigade-SD60 Maidstone-Date** DF133-Dennis-Magirus DL30U
ERH679Y		TL	83		Humberside Fire Brigade	C1 Peakes Lane-Grimsby- DF133-Carmichael-Magirus DL30U
FBV831Y	30110	TL	83		Lancashire County Fire Brigade	BD 71 Byrom Rd-Blackburn DF133-Carmichael-Magirus DL30
FBV832Y	30111	TL	83		Lancashire County Fire Brigade	CD 50 Blackpool Rd-Preston DF133-Carmichael-Magirus DL30
FBR221Y	200	TL	83		Durham Fire & Rescue Service-**1996** Durham County Fire & RB	Q1 St Cuthberts Way-Darlington DF133-Carmichael-Magirus DL30U
DWM603Y	1208	TL	83	94	Merseyside Metropolitan FB	N7 Manchester Rd-Southport-1989 Reserve-1994 **Ladder Re-chassied off AEC Mercury-OWM261** F125-Dennis-Merryweather-100'L
A49HKC	1220	TL	84		Merseyside Metropolitan FB	? **Ladder Re-chassied off AEC Mercury-KDJ404** F125-Dennis-Merryweather-100 L
A726BTY	364	TL	84		Tyne & Wear Metropolitan FB	**ex ND F The Fossway-Newcastle-1995**/ Reserve- DF133-Carmichael-Magirus DL30E
A618LWX		TL	84	95	West Yorkshire Fire Service	**ex AD Hunslett-1989**/AD Stanningley Rd-Bramley-Leeds DF133-Dennis-Magirus DL30E
A261PAG		TL	84		Humberside Fire Brigade	A1 Worship St-Hull DF133-Carmichael-Magirus DL30U

This Dennis DFS137 with a Magirus Turntable Ladder body is G782FWP, an appliance which replaced a long serving AEC Mercury/Merryweather TL, and is one of a pair with Hereford & Worcester Fire Brigade. The unit was delivered from Carmichael in 1990 and is based at Copenhagen Street in Worcester, though it served at Hereford, when the TL based there was damaged in a blaze at the Bulmer's factory in 1992.
Clive Shearman

Dennis F107 MHA599F was bodied by Carmichael's of Worcester to form a rare combination as most Magirus ladders were supplied with body work by David Haydon of Birmingham. The appliance was photographed at Oldbury in West Midlands Fire Service livery, though originally delivered as one of a pair to the Smethwick & West Bromwich Joint Fire Brigade. *Michael Lawmon*

B623AGE		TL	85	?	Strathclyde Fire Brigade (Scotland)	A1 Cowcaddens FS - **? Wdn after RTA** Dennis DF133- F&W Pierreville 100'L
B826CGA		TL	85		Strathclyde Fire Brigade (Scotland)	A5 Knighwood FS ? - A1 Cowcaddens - ? Dennis DF133- F&W Pierreville 100'L
B272BMB		TL	84		Cheshire Fire Brigade	B1 Winwick Rd-Warrington DF133-Carmichael-Magirus DL30E
B60FVK	371	TL	84		Tyne & Wear Metropolitan FB	ED M Station Rd-Fulwell-Sunderland DF133-Carmichael-Magirus DL30E
B767JTN	398	TL	85		Tyne & Wear Metropolitan FB	SD V Dryden Rd-Gateshead DF133-Carmichael-Magirus DL30E
B648GTN	191	TL	85		Durham Fire & Rescue Service-**1996** Durham County Fire & Rescue Brigade	G1 Finchale Rd-Framwellgate Moor-Durham DF133-Carmichael-Magirus DL30E
B642EET		TL	85		South Yorkshire County Fire Service	WD 13 Wellington St-Sheffield F125-Carmichael-Magirus LL-30
B925KWM	1231	TL	85	94	Merseyside Metropolitan FB	S6 High Park St-Toxteth-1992 Reserve-1994 **Ladder Re-chassied off AEC Mercury-HHF84** F125-Dennis-Merryweather-100'L
B593NPL	1241	TL	85	97	Merseyside Fire Brigade	C1 Studholme St-Bankhall / **ex Dennis SV Demonstrator** F127-John Dennis CB-Camiva EPA 30
C188EAG		TL	86		Humberside Fire Brigade	D1 Laneham St-Scunthorpe DF133-Angloco-Metz DLK30
C964JOK	115	TL	86		West Midlands Fire Service	**ex E1 Walsall-1993 /D2 Dudley Rd-Brierley Hill-1996** Reserve- Date DF133-Carmichael-Magirus DL30E
D886POO		TL	87		Essex County Fire &Rescue Service	C52 Broadmayne-Basildon-1991-**Ladders removed** **redesignated as Driver Training Vehicle** Dennis DFS135-G&T Power-Merryweather
D584OOP	113	TL	87		West Midlands Fire Service	A1 Lancaster Circus-Birmingham DF133-Carmichael-Magirus DL30E
E868JYV	TL48	TL	88		London Fire Brigade	**ex F22 Poplar-1991** /F29 Church Rd-Leyton- **Returned to France for repairs to ladder** F127-John Dennis CB-Camiva EPA 30
E869JYV	TL49	TL	88		London Fire Brigade	A24 Shaftsbury Ave-Soho F127-John Dennis CB-Camiva EPA 30

Delivered to Humberside Fire Brigade for service at Hull West station in 1984, Dennis DF133 A162PKH has Simon SS220 booms married to Dennis bodywork which was not untypical, but most Dennis Hydraulic Platforms use either the F125 or Delta II chassis. This machine is currently at the Peakes Lane station in Grimsby. *Ian Moore collection*

Dennis F127 Aerial Ladder Platform H411SUX is probably one of the few appliances that rarely saw operational action. It was delivered from Simon Engineering with a ST240 platform in 1991 for use at Shrewsbury where it is seen while in use on familiarity duties. Since that time it spent much time at Tweedale Fire Station, Telford, being replaced in 1997 by a new Volvo F10 appliance. *Clive Shearman*

E870JYV	TL50	TL	88	London Fire Brigade	**ex G33 High St-Kensington-1991**/G34 Kings Rd-Chelsea-F127-John Dennis CB-Camiva EPA 30
E783MRE	551	TL	88	Staffordshire Fire & Rescue Service	ND Lower Bethesda St-Hanley F127-John Dennis CB-Camiva EPA 30
F650JFJ	5308	TL	89	Devon Fire & Rescue Service	**17 Torquay-1992/02 Marlborough Rd-Ilfracombe-1996** 01 North Rd-Barnstaple-F127-John Dennis CB-Camiva EPA 30
G677FJW	119	TL	89	West Midlands Fire Service	**ex B3 Coventry-1992**/D1 Old Park Lane-Oldbury DF133-Carmichael DL30E
G779FWP		TL	90	Hereford & Worcester Fire Brigade	WD 46 Owen St-Hereford-**Damaged at serious Fire 1992** DFS137-Carmichael-Magirus DL30E
G782FWP		TL	90	Hereford & Worcester Fire Brigade	CD21 Copenhagen St-Worcester DFS137-Carmichael-Magirus DL30E
H207MOK	122	TL	91	West Midlands Fire Service	A6 Washwood Heath Rd-Ward End DF237-Carmichael-Magirus DL30E

					Dennis F Series Chassied Hydraulic Platforms	
9750KF	1049	PHP	63	84	Liverpool Fire Brigade	#2 Belvidere Rd-Liverpool-1974/S4 Belvidere Rd-1975 C1 Studholme St-Bankhall-Liverpool-1983-Merseyside FB **Booms Re-chassied onto Dennis F125-Dennis B923KWM** F117-Dennis-Simon SS65
KLV812E	1066	PHP	67	83	Liverpool Fire Brigade	#2 Belvidere Rd-Liverpool-1969 #12 Studholme St-Bankhall-Liverpool-1974 C3 Canning Place-Liverpool-1983-Merseyside FB **Booms Re-chassied onto Dennis F125-Dennis-A48HKC** F37-Dennis-Simon SS65
JJV999F		PHP	68	83	Grimsby County Borough Fire Brigade	Peakes Lane-Grimsby-1974 / C1 Grimsby- 1977 A4 New Walkergate-Beverley-Humberside Fire Brigade F38-Dennis-Simon SS50
VLU214G		HP	68	95	Fire Service College	FSC Moreton in Marsh-Gloucestershire-1982 **Sold to Bedfordshire F&RS** F119-Dennis-Simon SS70
HEM698H	1093	PHP	70	83	Bootle County Borough Fire Brigade	The Strand-Bootle-1974 /C5 The Strand-Bootle-1979 Reserve-1984-Merseyside FB F119-Carmichael-Orbitor 72'
VKD958H	55 1098	PHP	70	82	Liverpool Fire Brigade	#17 Canning Place-1974/C3 Canning Place-Liverpool-1979 Reserve-1982-Merseyside FB F44-Dennis-Simon SS50
DWY745H		PHP	70	83	West Riding of Yorkshire FB	Batley Fire Station-1974/B4 Union Rd-Thorne-1984 South Yorkshire County FS F45-Dennis-Simon SS50
WKK964J		PHP	71	?	Kent Fire Brigade	45 Watling St-Rochester-Medway-? F45-Dennis-Simon SS50
RFY33J	1106	PHP	71	80	Southport County Borough FB	Manchester Rd-Southport-1974 N7 Manchester Rd-Southport-1978 Reserve-Merseyside FB F108-Dennis-Simon SS50
LFM673J		PHP	71	86	City of Chester	St Annes St-Chester-1981/Reserve-Cheshire Fire Brigade **Sold to Hoistline Ltd-Isle of Man-Re reg UMN999** F108-Dennis-Simon SS50
FDA699J	238	PHP	71	81	Wolverhampton County Borough FB	Merridale St-Wolverhampton-1974/ E5 Wolverhampton-1981 West Midlands Fire Service F108-Dennis-Simon SS50
XKA532J	1102	PHP	71	80	City of Liverpool Fire Brigade	12 Studholme St-Bankhall- Liverpool-1974 C1Bankhall-1980 /Merseyside Fire Brigade F45-HCB Angus-Simon SS50
JVT699K		PHP	71	86	City of Stoke on Trent Fire Brigade	Lower Bethesda St-Hanley-1974 /ND Hanley-1977 ND Knutton Lane-Newcastle under Lyne-1986 **Sold to Tralee-Kerry County-Irish Republic-304CIN** F109-Dennis-Simon SS50
FKN291L		PHP	72	?	Kent Fire Brigade	80 Upper Bridge St-Canterbury-? F49-Dennis-Simon SS50
HWN771L		PHP	72	90	Swansea County Borough FB (Wales)	#1 Grove Place-1974 / 5 Grove Place-West Glamorgan CFS F45-Dennis-Simon SS50
SWJ76L		PHP	73	86	City of Sheffield	Elm Lane-Sheffield-1974 / E2 Elm Lane-South Yorkshire F108-Dennis-Simon SS50
LNV211L		HP	73	90	Northamptonshire Fire Brigade	A2 Forest Gate Rd-Corby F123-Dennis-Simon SS70
ODC234L	34	HP	73	94	Tees-side Fire Brigade	#1 Park Road South-Middlesbrough-1974 S1 Middlesbrough-1988/Reserve-1991-Cleveland CFS **Sold to Felixstowe Docks** F123 Dennis-Simon SS85
SEO545M		PHP	73	86	Barrow in Furrness County Borough FB	Abbey Rd-Barrow in Furness-1974 /BD Barrow-1980 BD Mill Lane-Walney-1986-Cumbria FS F108-Dennis-Simon SS50

The rare Dennis F119 chassis is seen here in combination with Simon SS70 booms on Hydraulic Platform VLU214G. It was delivered in 1968 to the Home Office Fire Service College in Moreton in Marsh, Gloucestershire and was sold in 1982 to the Bedfordshire Fire Service. In the early 1990s though there was a problem with the Scania and Dennis Platforms at Luton and Bedford being damaged in accidents during which a former Dennis platform from Cleveland Fire Brigade and VLU214G provided cover while the others were repaired. *David Thomas*

POA337M	59	HP	73	94	City of Birmingham	Icknield Port Rd-Ladywood-1974 /C07 Ladywood-1978 C04 Bristol Rd-Bournbrook-1989/Res-1994/ West Midlands F123-Dennis-Simon SS85
XTH857M		PHP	73	93	Carmarthen & Cardiganshire (Wales)	High St-Pembroke Dock-1974 B6 Pembroke Dock-1993 /Dyfed Fire Brigade F108-Dennis-Simon SS50
TLO102M		HP	73		GLC London Fire Brigade	**Ordered for the LFB-Not accepted-Sold Singapore** F123-Dennis-Simon SS70
RUP529M	193	PHP	74	84	Durham County Fire Brigade	C21 Surtees Rd-Peterlee-1984 **Sold to Castlebar-County Mayo-Ireland / Re-reg-EIS78** F48-Dennis-Simon SS50
DDC1 NPY906P	23	HP	76	95	Cleveland County Fire Brigade	**Registration number from earlier Dennis F12 Pump/E** #2 South Rd-Norton-Stockton-1990 **Sold to Bedfordshire F&RS and re-registered** F123-Dennis-Simon SS220
ORH40P		HP	76	93	Humberside Fire Brigade	D2 Larsen Rd-Goole Delta 2-Dennis-Simon SS220
ORH41P		HP	76	93	Humberside Fire Brigade	C1 Peaks Lane-Grimsby-1983 Reserve-1994 Delta 2-Dennis-Simon SS220
SNV403R		HP	77	91	Northamptonshire Fire Brigade	B1 The Mounts-Northampton F123-Dennis-Simon SS220
OUV291R	HP2	HP	77	91	GLC London Fire Brigade	C26 Milton Court-Moor Lane-Barbican F123-Dennis-Simon SS70
WNU799S		HP	78		Nottinghamshire Fire Brigade	**ex B21 Abbey St-Dunkirk-Nottingham-1993**/ Reserve- Delta 2-Dennis-Simon SS220
VWG511S		HP	78		South Yorkshire County Fire Service	**ex WD23 Darnell Rd-Sheffield-1988** ED1 Broadway-Barnsley- Delta 2-Dennis-Simon SS263
PEY254S		HP	78		Clwyd County Fire Service-**1996** North Wales Fire Service (Wales)	**ex E1 Wrexham-1992/W1 Coast Rd-Rhyl-1994**/Reserve- Delta 2-Dennis-Simon SS263
TCR354T	A00063	HP	79		West Sussex Fire Brigade	17 Northgate-Chichester Delta 2-Dennis-Simon SS220
YEP817T		HP	79	91	West Glamorgan County FS (Wales)	#1 Cimla Rd-Neath **Booms Re-chassied off Commer VAC-Evans-DTG101C** F123-Dennis-Simon SS65
RUY150V		HP	80	96	Hereford & Worcester Fire Brigade	ND 24 Castle Rd-Kidderminster F125-Dennis-Simon SS263
KKK252V	194	HP	80	96	Kent Fire Brigade	**ex 43 Watling St-Rochester-Medway-1995**/ Reserve- F125-Dennis-Simon SS220
OAG10V		HP	80		Humberside Fire Brigade	**ex A3 Hull West-1983 /ex B3 Hull Bransholme-1992** D2 M62 Industrial Estate-Goole- Delta 2-Dennis-Simon SS220
WFM464W		HP	81		Cheshire Fire Brigade	C8 Chester Rd-Macclesfield F125-Dennis-Simon SS263
WFM465W		HP	81		Cheshire Fire Brigade	**ex A1 Chester-1989** /Reserve- F125-Dennis-Simon SS263
UVS196W		HP	81	95	Buckinghamshire Fire Brigade	**ex Childs Way-Broughton-1989** **Booms Re-chassied onto Volvo FL6-18-M164SWL** F125-Dennis-Simon SS220
VRO119W		HP	81		Bedfordshire Fire Brigade	**ex 01 Bedford-1993 /Damaged in RTA-Written off** F125-Dennis-Simon SS263
MKE883W		HP	81	?	Kent Fire Brigade	60 Loose Rd-Maidstone **Withdrawn** F125-Dennis- **EPL Firecracker 235**
MKE884W		HP	81	?	Kent Fire Brigade	16 Ladywell-Dover **Withdrawn** F125-Dennis-**EPL Firecracker 235**
MKE885W		HP	81	?	Kent Fire Brigade	80 Upper Bridge St-Canterbury **Withdrawn** F125-Dennis- **EPL Firecracker 235**

FPO23X	A00064	HP	81		West Sussex Fire Brigade	12 Hurst Rd-Horsham **Delta 2**-Dennis-Simon SS220	
XCL21X		HP	82		Norfolk Fire Service	AD 27 Bethel St-Norwich F125-Dennis-Simon SS220	
XCL22X		HP	82	90	Norfolk Fire Service	C69 Friars Lane-Great Yarmouth **Booms Re-chassied off ERF84PS-Jennings-JCL999G Sold to Simon Engineering** F125-Dennis-Simon SS70	
RLJ999X		HP	82	88	Dorset Fire Brigade	B23 Alumhurst Rd-Westbourne-Bournemouth **Booms Re-ch onto Volvo FL6-17-HCB A -E50MEL** F125-Dennis-Simon SS263	
ACM413X	1207	HP	82		Merseyside Fire Brigade	**ex W1 Exmouth St-Birkenhead-1994**/ Reserve- F125-Dennis-Simon SS263	
MFS104X		HP	82		Lothian & Borders Fire Brigade (Scotland)	**ex 31 Sighthill-Edinburgh-1994** /Reserve- F125-Dennis-Simon SS263	
NYV773Y	HP13P	HP	83		GLC London Fire Brigade	**ex L25/F41 Dagenham-1990**/H31 Old Town-Croydon- F125-Dennis-Simon SS220	
NYV774Y	HP14P	HP	83		GLC London Fire Brigade	**ex C26/A29 Barbican-1990**/NW Area-Reserve- F125-Dennis-Simon SS220	
NYV775Y	HP15P	HP	83		GLC London Fire Brigade	E22 Blissett St-Greenwich F125-Dennis-Simon SS220	
A48HKC	1221	HP	84		Merseyside Fire Brigade	**ex E1 Parr Stocks Rd-St Helens-1994**/ Reserve- **Booms Re-chassied off Dennis F117-Dennis-KLV812E** F125-Dennis-Simon SS65	
A162PKH		HP	84		Humberside Fire Brigade	**ex A3 Hull West-1992** /C1 Peakes Lane-Grimsby- DF133-Dennis-Simon SS220	
B923KWM	1229	HP	85		Merseyside Fire Brigade	Reserve-1995 **Booms Re-chassied off Dennis F117-Dennis-9750KF** F125-Dennis-Simon SS65	
B369OFA	503	HP	84		Staffordshire Fire Brigade	**ND Springfield Rd-Leek-1995** ND Uttoexter Rd-Longton- **ex Dennis SV Demonstrator** F127-Dennis-Simon SS220	
B538GWB		HP	85		South Yorkshire County Fire Service	WD 13 Wellington St-Sheffield F127-Saxon-Simon SS263	
C342WHA	W078	HP	85		Hertfordshire County Council Fire Brigade	C23 St George's Way-Stevenage F127-Saxon-Simon SS263	
D302OWA		HP	86		South Yorkshire County Fire Service	WD 24 Elm Lane-Sheffield F127-Saxon-Simon SS220	
D368JNX		HP	87		Mid Glamorgan Fire Service-**1996** South Wales Fire Service (Wales)	WD 01 Angel St-Bridgend F127-Saxon-Simon SS263	
E568DMJ	W080	HP	88		Hertfordshire County Council Fire Brigade	A09 Whippendell Rd-Watford F127-Saxon-Simon SS263	
F25OCR	A00062	HP	89		West Sussex Fire Brigade	01 Ardsheal Rd-Worthing F127-Saxon-Simon SS263	
G314WNM	W083	HP	90		Hertfordshire County Council Fire Brigade	B11 Harpenden Rd-St Albans F127-Gloster Saro-Simon SS263	
G999NCH	HP-03	ALP	90		Derbyshire Fire Service	**ex D01 Ascot Drive-Derby-1996** D03 Kingsway-Derby- F127-Saxon-Simon ST240-S	
G999NRB	HP-04	ALP	90		Derbyshire Fire Service	B01 Campton Grove-Buxton F127-Saxon-Simon ST240-S	
H411SUX		ALP	91		Shropshire Fire & Rescue Service	St Michael's St-Shrewsbury/**Stored at Tweedale** **This machine has been in store since its delivery.** F127-Saxon-Simon ST240-S	
H501DND		HP	91		Greater Manchester County Fire Service	A15 Park Rd-Stretford F127-Saxon-Simon SS263	

Chassis		N 1.5 t Ace Big 4 Big 6 F12 F106 RS-SS			Dennis Chassied Emergency/Rescue Tenders Engine/Chassis 6.6 litre P/4.5 tons 4 cyl P/1.5 tons 4 cyl P/ 4 cyl P/ 6 cyl P/ B80 P/12ft 6ins T6 Perkins P/ Cummins/Perkins	The chassis specifications have changed over the years to suit the size of ET purchased. Normally Pump chassis are sufficient to cover the needs.
XV3953		ET	28	47	LCC London Fire Brigade	1 Southwark Bridge Rd-Southwark N Series-Dennis
UF3803		ET	28	58	Brighton Fire Brigade	Brighton Fire Station-1938 /Preston Circus-Brighton-1958 1.5 Ton-Limousine
GP9015	3-ET	ET	31	59	LCC London Fire Brigade	B66/B20 Roseberry Ave-Clerkenwell-1948 Big Six-Limousine
JD3659		ET	33	59	West Ham County Borough FB	Prince Regent Lane-Plaistow-1959-**Light Blue livery** Big Six-Limousine
?		ET	34	58	City of Sheffield	#1 Division St-Sheffield Ace-Limousine
?		ET	34	60	Cambridgeshire Fire Brigade	St Andrews-Cambridge/Parkside-Cambridge-1960 **Converted from Limousine Pump** Ace-Limousine
FMF957		P/ET	36	56	Ealing County Borough Fire Brigade	60 Uxbridge Rd-Ealing-1948 72 High St-Southall-Middlesex FB Big Six-Limousine
AHJ702		E/ST	36	63	Southend on Sea County Borough FB	London Rd-Southend-1963 Big Six-Limousine

An example of a Dennis Big Six chassis is seen here as an Emergency Salvage Tender. The 1936 appliance AHJ702 ran from the London Road fire station in Southend and served that station for nearly 30 years being replaced by a Dennis F106 in 1964. *Keith Wardell collection*

GGT716	AEL-1	ET	41	62	LCC London Fire Brigade	D61 Albert Embankment-Lambeth-1955 **Converted into Foam Tender** /C42 Evelyn St-Deptford-1962 Falcon-LFB
FRJ928		ET	53	72	City of Salford	The Crescent-Salford-1972 F12-Carmichael
OZ9605		ET	54	?	Belfast Fire Brigade (Northern Ireland)	**Fire station ?** F17-Dennis
OZ9606		ET	54	?	Belfast Fire Brigade (Northern Ireland)	**Fire station ?** F17-Dennis
GVD777		ET	56	80	Lanarkshire Fire Brigade (Scotland)	Dellburn St-Motherwell - 1975 Strathclyde Fire Brigade F12-Dennis
51CMX	ET-3	ET	57	72	Middlesex Fire Brigade (Ambulance Service)	39 Harrow Rd-Wembley-1965/G30 Wembley-1968 J27 North Circular Rd-Finchley-1972 London FB F12-Dennis
RZ1057		ET	57	?	Belfast Fire Brigade (Northern Ireland)	Central Fire Station -Belfast F12-Dennis
VVC898	105	ET	58	80	City of Coventry	#1 Hales St-Coventry-1967 /#1 Hales St-1974 **Converted Control Unit**/C01 Radford Rd-Coventry-1976 C04 Hipswell Way-Binley-1980 West Mid'sFS/ **Preserved** F12-Dennis
RWA444		ET	58	68	City of Sheffield	#1 Division St-Sheffield-1968 /**Written off in RTA** F12-Carmichael
LSA7		ET	55	74	North Eastern Area Fire Brigade (Scotland)	King St-Aberdeen/Friars Rd-Elgin F12-Dennis
6864DT		ET	?	67?	Doncaster County Borough Fire Brigade	**Believed written off in RTA** F Series-no detail's known
512CKA	1011	ET	60	80	City of Liverpool	#1 Hatton Gardens-Liverpool-1969 #12-Studholme St-Bankhall-1974 /C1 Bankhall-1980-Merseyside MFB F103-Dennis

Dennis F12 51CMX, an Emergency Tender, was new to Harrow Road fire station at Wembley in 1957. It later moved to Finchley, another former Middlesex station that had become part of the London Fire Brigade in 1965. The F12 was a popular pumping appliance with much of the country seeing an example though, as a specialist appliance it was less common. There were only seven delivered as Emergency Tenders.
Keith Wardell collection

567DZ		ET	60	?	Belfast Fire Brigade (Northern Ireland)	Londonderry Fire Station F28-Dennis
VYE235	ET7A	ET	59	79	LCC London Fire Brigade	D61-Lambeth-1965/B22 Albert Embankment-Lambeth-1979 F103-Dennis
337ALX	ET8B	ET	61	82	LCC London Fire Brigade	C43/E22 Woolwich Rd-East Greenwich-1972 E21 High St-Lewisham-1979/Reserve-1982 CV31-Dennis
338ALX	ET9B	ET	61	82	LCC London Fire Brigade	A4/A23 Euston Rd-Euston-1972 A21 Harrow Rd-Paddington-1978/Reserve-1982 CV31-Dennis
9012LV	S4 1052	ET	64	84	City of Liverpool	#6 Banks Rd-Liverpool-1974 S4 Banks Rd-Merseyside FB-1984 Pax V-Dennis
AJN384B		ET Salv/T	64	87	Southend County Borough FB	Sutton Rd-Southend-1974 /B30 Sutton Rd-1976 B31 Mountdale Gardens-Leigh on Sea-Southend-1985 Reserve-1987-Essex County FB F106-Dennis
EBB783C	113	ET	65	83	Newcastle & Gateshead Joint Fire Service	A1 Pilgrim St-Newcastle Central-1974 T Victoria Rd-Hebburn-1977 /E High St-Gosforth-1983 Tyne & Wear MFB-**Preserved** F107-Dennis
DKD929C	1048	ET	65	82	City of Liverpool	#9 Longmoor Lane-Fazakerly-1968/#13 Storrington Ave-1974 N3 Storrington Ave-Merseyside FB F107-Dennis
HUH314D	10	ET	66	87	City of Cardiff (Wales)	#1 Westgate St-Cardiff-1973/#1 Adam St-Cardiff-1974 1 Adam St-1982/**Converted Fire Prevention Unit** 2 Colchester Ave-Roath-Cardiff-1987 South Glamorgan CFS/**Preserved** F107-Dennis
ODT671E		ET	67	83	Doncaster County Borough FB	Ledger Way-Doncaster-1974 B1 Ledger Way-1983-South Yorkshire CFS/**Short WB** F106-Dennis
ALT470H	510	ET	70	83	Fire Service College	FSC Moreton in Marsh-Gloucestershire F108-Dennis
BLO801H (later FYY37H)	ET12A	ET	70	93	GLC London Fire Brigade	C27 Rosebury Ave-Clerkenwell-1977 Reserve-1993 F108-Dennis
ADC999K	28	Res/T	72	86	Tees-side Fire Brigade	1 Park Road South-Middlesbrough-1974 S1 Middlesbrough-1985 S8 Bickley Way-Coulby Newham-1986-Cleveland County FB **Converted by Tees-side Polytechnic** F108-Dennis
LHF75K	1111	ET	72	85	Wallasey County Borough FB	Mill Lane-Wallasey-1974 W6 Wallasey-Merseyside FB-1985 F48-Dennis
JHX13K	ET13A	ET	72	94	GLC London Fire Brigade	J27 North Circular Rd-Finchley-1977 A21 Harrow Rd-Paddington-1982 /Reserve-1994 F108-Dennis
JHX14K	ET14A	ET	72	94	GLC London Fire Brigade	H31 Old Town-Croydon-1978/H32 London Rd-Norbury-1977 Reserve-1984 /H32 London Rd-Norbury-**ERT duties due to OYT511R being written off in RTA** F108-Dennis
XBA327K		ET SalvT	72	83?	City of Salford	The Crescent-Salford F48-Dennis
WDW202K		ET & Res/T	72	91	Newport County Borough FB (Wales)	01 Malpas Rd-Newport-1974/B09 Malpas Rd-1981 **Converted Chemical Incident Unit** C01 Darren Drive-Abercarn-1983 B19 New Rd-New Inn-Pontypool-1986 Gwent FB F48-Dennis

Photographed at the 1993 FSPG Rally at Chacewater in Staffordshire was Dennis F106 EBB783C, a regular on the rally scene. It was delivered to the Newcastle & Gateshead Joint Fire Service in 1965 and served at the Pilgrim Street station in Newcastle. It originally sported the distinctive maroon and red livery associated with that service, which disappeared on amalgamation with the Tyne & Wear Metropolitan Fire Brigade in 1974. *Clive Shearman*

H49KVN	3	ET C/Unit	90		Cleveland County Fire Brigade-**1996** Cleveland Fire Brigade	9 Stranton West Hartlepool **Body used to extend, now glued shut/Re-bodied at JDC** DF237-John Dennis CB
H912TUY		ISU	91		Hereford & Worcester Fire Brigade	26 Friar St-Droitwich SS237-John Dennis CB
H276HVX		MRT	91		Essex County Fire & Rescue Service	D70 Fourth Ave-Harlow SS235-John Dennis CB
K263YPY		ET	92		North Yorkshire Fire & Rescue Service	E11 Crosby Rd-Northallerton DS153-HCB Angus
L516XBB	082	SIU	94		Durham Fire & Rescue Service-**1996** Durham County Fire & Rescue Brigade	G1 Finchale Rd-Durham SS235-Devcoplan
M225PHN	26	Heavy Rec/V	95		Cleveland County Fire & Rescue-**1996** Cleveland Fire Brigade	2 South Rd-Stockton /**Atlas AS80.1-Crane** SS235-John Dennis CB
M919SVN	16	ET DC/Unit	95		Cleveland County Fire & Rescue-**1996** Cleveland Fire Brigade	8 Newham Way-Coulby Newham SS235-John Dennis CB

					Dennis Chassied Specialist Appliances	All types of chassis were used on the appliances featured below. Many were custom built machines, whilst others were old pumps which were re bodied and used for other specialist roles.
BYV317	BL.11	Rec/V	36	56	LCC London Fire Brigade	D61 Albert Embankment-Lambeth **Crane re-chassied onto Dennis F23 SLD661** Lancet -Herbert Morris Crane
BYV318	Cav-1	CAV	35	65	LCC London Fire Brigade	D61 Albert Embankment-Lambeth 45cwt-
DGJ308	HL-1	HLL	36	?	LCC London Fire Brigade	D61 Albert Embankment-Lambeth /**1..5 mile of hose.** Lancet-
CDM317		F/SalvT	38	72	County of Flintshire Fire Brigade (Wales)	Chester Rd-Queensferry Limousine
GGT716		FOT	41	62	LCC London Fire Brigade	**ex ET D61-Lambeth-1955** /C42 Evelyn St-Deptford-1962 Falcon-LFB
FKY719		FOT	49	74	City of Bradford	**ex Pump/E-1963-**Nelson St-Bradford F7-Dennis-CoB FB-**Named 'John McHugh'**
DEE109		FOT	52	75	Grimsby County Borough Fire Brigade	**ex Pump/E- ?** / Peakes Lane-1975-Humberside FB F12-Dennis-GCB FB
991BRF		F/Salv/T C/Unit	54	**74?**	Staffordshire Fire Brigade	**ex Pump/E-Darleston-?** / Blue Lane West-Walsall CB F12-Dennis-WCB
RLV149	2001	Rec/V	54	83	City of Liverpool	**ex Pump/E #1 Hatton Gardens-1969** /Brigade Workshops Merseyside Fire Brigade F12-Dennis/CLFB
STT319		HLL	55	85	Devon County Fire Brigade	**ex Water Tender-1975** 01 North Rd-Barnstaple F8-Dennis
SLD661	BL.13	Rec/V	56	60	LCC London Fire Brigade	Brigade Workshops-Lambeth/**Crane from BYV317 Written off after accident with RSJ** F23-Dennis-Herbert Morris Crane
LVG799		Salv/T	58	71	City of Norwich	**ex Pump-1961-**Bethel Street-Norwich F25-Dennis
HTS163		F/SalvT	58	?	Angus Area Fire Brigade (Scotland)	A11 Kingsway East-Dundee-1975 F24-Dennis-TFB
ONR4 (later CJF613B)		Rec/V	58	?	City of Leicester	**ex WRL-** Brigade Workshops F25A-LFS

London Fire Brigade operated four Dennis Pax IV appliances. Delivered in 1962 were two Dennis-bodied Foam Tenders which were based at Deptford and 302CXM, seen here, operating out of Este Road in Battersea. In 1963, Carmichael delivered two Hose Layers for use at Chelsea fire station and Lea Green. The London Fire Brigade ordered further special appliances on the Dennis chassis, though these were on the F Series. *The late Alan Batchelor*

301CXM	FT-1	FOT	62	78	LCC London Fire Brigade	C42/B27 Evelyn St-Deptford PaxIV-Dennis
302CXM	FT-2	FOT	62	79	LCC London Fire Brigade	D71/K23 Este Rd-Battersea PaxIV-Dennis
303CXM	HL-3	HLL	63	79	LCC London Fire Brigade	A8/A27 Kings Rd-Chelsea-1977/H32 Thornton Heath-1979 PaxIV-Carmichael
304CXM	HL-4	HLL	63	82	LCC London Fire Brigade	C49/E29 Eltham Rd-Lee Green Pax IV-Carmichael

3200KB	1019	C/Unit	63	88	City of Liverpool	#1 Hatton Gardens-Liverpool-1969 #1 Studholme St-Bankhall-1974/C1 Studholme St-1982 **Conv Chemical Incident Unit** N3 Storington Ave-Liverpool-1988 Pax IV-Dennis
314FLM	BL.14	Rec/V	64	77	LCC London Fire Brigade	B21 Old Town-Clapham F107-Dennis-Herbert Morris Crane
CVP923C	100	Rec/V	65	84	City of Birmingham	1 Lancaster Circus-Central-1974 A1 Lancaster Circus-Central-1984/West Midlands FS F37-Dennis-Holmes
DKD928C	44 1058	Hi ex FOT	65	84	City of Liverpool	**ex Pump/E #6 Banks Rd-1970** **ex PE #1 Hatton Gardens-1969** C1 Studholme St Bankhall -1984 F106-Dennis/CLFB
EYF689J	4	Salv/T	70	80	London Salvage Corps	Aldersgate London D-Dennis
DHN999J	6 210	Rec/V	70	96	Darlington County Borough Fire Brigade	S1 Borough Rd-Darlington-1972 S1 St Cuthberts Way-Darlington-1974 S1 Darlington-Date/Durham County FB -**Preserved** Maxim-Dial Holmes 750
WDW202K		Res/T	71	89	Newport County Borough (Wales)	1 Malpas Rd-Newport-1974 **Conv Chemical Incident Unit**/B9 Malpas Rd-Newport-1981 C1 Darren Drive-Abercarn-1983 B19 New Rd-New Inn-Pontypool-1989 Gwent Fire Brigade F48-Dennis
JDM529K		FOT	71	89	County of Flint FB (Wales)	E2 Chester Rd-Deeside-1974/E2 Chester Rd-Deeside-1977 E1 Bradley Rd-Wrexham-1989/County of Clwyd FB F48-Dennis
PPT423K	098	FOT	72	88	Durham County Fire Brigade	**ex WRL S5-1981** /N6 Surtees Rd-Peterlee-1988 D Series-Dennis-DCFB
UTP78K		WRC	72	?	Hampshire Fire Service	**ex WRL B24-Southsea-1984**/D47 Station Rd-Fordingbridge F108-Hampshire FBWS
JLT11K	HL-11	HLL	72	84	GLC London Fire Brigade	K30 Burlington Rd-New Malden -1982 K28 St Dunstans Hill-Sutton-1984 F108-Dennis
JLT12K	HL-12	HLL	72	83	GLC London Fire Brigade	G21 Pinner Rd-Harrow-1981 G22 Honey Pot Lane-Stanmore-1983 F108-Dennis
JLT13K	HL-13	HLL	72	85	GLC London Fire Brigade	J24 Forest Rd-Walthamstow-1985 F108-Dennis
JLT14K	HL-14	HLL	72	83	GLC London Fire Brigade	G24 The Boroughs-Hendon-1982 E29 Eltham Rd-Lee Green-1983 F108-Dennis
AVW980L		FoT Simoniter	73	89	Essex County Fire Brigade	B27/C52 Broadmayne-Basildon F48-Dennis-Simon TSM15
PGN15L	HL-15	HLL	73	85	GLC London Fire Brigade	L27 Alfreds Way-Barking-1982 F21 Romford Rd-Stratford-1985 F108-Dennis
TLO9M	FT-9	FOT	73	92	GLC London Fire Brigade	L21 High St-East Ham-1978/G21 Pinner Rd-Harrow-1992 F108-Dennis
MAR799P		FoT Simoniter	76	87	Essex County Fire Brigade	B30/C50 Hogg Lane-Grays F48-Dennis-Simon TSM15
NTJ89S	1156	Decon Unit	77		Merseyside Fire Brigade	**ex WRL N3 Storrington Ave-1988** N3 Storrington Ave-Liverpool R133-Nova Scotia
NHF283S	1148	Hi ex FOT	77		Merseyside Fire Brigade	**ex WRL S4 High Park St-1984** /S9 Belle Vale-Liverpool R133-Nova Scotia
THL78S		FOT	77	94	South Yorkshire County Fire Service	ED20 Knolbeck Lane-Brampton Bierlow Delta 2-Dennis

Reg	Fleet	Type	In	Out	Brigade	Notes
UYU727S	FT-11	FOT	78	93?	GLC London Fire Brigade	D27 London Rd-Heston-1983/D28 Faggs Rd-Feltham- F131-Merryweather
UYU728S	FT-12	FOT	78	93?	GLC London Fire Brigade	K23 Este Rd-Battersea F131-Merryweather
UYU729S	FT-13	FOT	78	93?	GLC London Fire Brigade	J21 Church St-Edmonton F131-Merryweather
UYU730S	FT-14	FOT	78	93?	GLC London Fire Brigade	L27 Alfreds Way-Barking F131-Merryweather
UVP96S	7	FOT	78	91	West Midlands Fire Service	A3 Lichfield Rd-Sutton Coldfield Delta 2-Dennis
DBR947S	042	FOT	78	94	Durham County Fire Brigade	**ex WRL N1-1980-S8-1988/N6 Town Centre-Peterlee-1995** D Series-Dennis-DCFB
EFM561S		FOT	78		Cheshire Fire Brigade	A2 Wellington Rd-Ellesmere Port Delta 2-Dennis
EFM562S		FOT	78		Cheshire Fire Brigade	B2 Winwick St-Warrington Delta 2-Dennis
LGR912T	089	BAT	78	95	Durham County Fire Brigade	**ex WRL N1-1981-N4-1986/N1 Finchale Rd-Durham-1985** D Series-Dennis-DCFB
DOJ115V	109	F/SalvT	79	92	West Midlands Fire Service	Hipswell Highway-Binley Delta 2-Dennis
DOJ116V	110	F/SalvT	79	93	West Midlands Fire Service	C8 Brook Lane-Billesley-1984-**Conv to BAT-C/Unit** A1 Lancaster Circus-Central Delta 2-Dennis
KRH582V		FOT	79		Humberside Fire Brigade	B2 Noodle Hill Way-Bransholme Delta 2-Dennis
SDM556V		FOT	80	95	Cheshire County Fire Brigade	**ex WRL** /C1 Macon Way-Crewe RS133-Dennis-CFB
EBB846W	319	C/Unit	80		Tyne & Wear Metropolitan FB	A West Denton Way-West Denton Dominator-Angloco
MKE909W		FOT	81	95	Kent Fire Brigade	**ex WRL** /39 Gravesend Rd-Strood RS133-Dennis-KFB
HAB900X		WRC FOC	81		Hereford & Worcester Fire Brigade	WD 46 Owen St-Hereford DFS133-Dennis
FPO24X	A00057	FOT	81		West Sussex Fire Brigade	05 Stoney Lane-Shoreham by the Sea DFS133-Dennis
RHN896X	14	FOT	82		Cleveland County Fire Brigade-**1996** Cleveland Fire Brigade	7 Seaton Carew Rd-Billingham DFS133-Dennis
HFM710X		HRV	82		Cheshire Fire Brigade	**ex WRL-A4 Northwich-1996**-B1 Winwick St-Warrington RS133-Dennis-CFB-**Moffat Mounty**
ACH449Y	WC-04	WRC	83		Derbyshire Fire Service	C01 Sheffield Rd-Chesterfield DFS133-Dennis
CHA755Y	111	Rec/V	67 83		West Midlands Fire Service	**ex ERF chassied HP D2 Brierley Hill-1983** A5 College Rd-Perry Barr R-ERF-Bro-Wrecker/WMFS
A204YCU	345	FOT	83		Tyne & Wear Metropolitan FB	**ex N Sunderland-1992** /V Dryden Rd-Gateshead DF133-Chubb FP
A951XOB	301	PMover	84	95	West Midlands Fire Service	B7 Northway-NEC-Bickenhill Delta 1616-Multilift-Keyway
A952XOB	302	PMover	84	95	West Midlands Fire Service	**B7-NEC-Bickenhill-1994** /C9 Speedwell Rd-Hay Mills Delta 1616-Multilift-Keyway
A953XOB	303	PMover	84	95	West Midlands Fire Service	Reserve Delta 1616-Multilift-Keyway
A954XOB	304	PMover	84		West Midlands Fire Service	**ex Reserve /Converted to 6x2 for HGV Training** C3 Stoney Lane-Smethwick- Delta 1616-Multilift-Keyway
A955XOB	305	PMover	84	94	West Midlands Fire Service	D8 Hargate Lane-West Bromwich **Sold to Wiltshire FB-4/5 Warminster-** Delta 1616-Multilift-Keyway
A956XOB	306	PMover	84	95	West Midlands Fire Service	**ex D8-West Bromwich-1994**/E3 Clarks Lane-Willenhall Delta 1616-Multilift-Keyway

A957XOB	307	PMover	84		West Midlands Fire Service	**ex Reserve-1994** / E1 Blue Lane West-Walsall Delta 1616-Multilift-Keyway
B229VRH		FOT	85		Humberside Fire Brigade	C4 Pelham Rd-Immingham DF133-Dennis
B759GCN	373	PMover IS/Boat	84		Tyne & Wear Metropolitan Fire Brigade	**ex Pump/L**-F Walker-Newcastle- SS133-Dennis-T&W MFB
C45ORA	BA-05	BAT	86		Derbyshire Fire Service	**ex C01 Sheffield Rd-Chesterfield-1995**/ Reserve- DF135-Cottingham
D482RKW		BAT	87		South Yorkshire County Fire Service	28 Edlington Lane-Edlington RS135-Carmichael
D892DDC		FOT	86		Cleveland County Fire Brigade-**1996** Cleveland Fire Brigade	3 Trunk Rd-Grangetown SS135-Saxon
D892POO		FOT	87		Essex County Fire Service	**C52 Broadmayne-Basildon -96** / D70 Fourth Ave-Harlow DF135-Carmichael
E885ANO		FOT	87		Essex County Fire Service	**C50 Hogg Lane-Grays-1996** / C52 Broadmayne-Basildon DF135-Carmichael
G551XWK	PM-1	PMover ET	89		Warwickshire Fire & Rescue Service	20 Newtown Rd-Nuneaton **Pod system height lowered due to RTA** DFS237-Multilift-Transliner
G552XWK	PM-2	PMover ET	89		Warwickshire Fire & Rescue Service	29 Royal Leamington Spa **Pod system height lowered due to RTA** DFS237-Multilift-Transliner
G553XWK	PM-3	PMover FoT/WRC	89		Warwickshire Fire & Rescue Service	22 Park Rd-Coleshill DFS237-Multilift-Transliner/Whale
H751SNT	90	PMover TSU	91		Shropshire Fire & Rescue Service	Stafford Park-Telford-1992 /Haybridge Rd-Wellington SS234-Torton-Macdonald Kane
H653JKF	1279	PMover CIU	91		Merseyside Fire Brigade	**ex N2 Longmoor Lane-Fazackerley-1995**/Reserve- DFS237-Multilift-Cocker
H654JKF	1280	PMover SRU	91		Merseyside Fire Brigade	**ex E5 Millfields-Eccleston-St Helens-1995**/ Reserve- DFS237-Multilift-Cocker
J256KWM	1281	PMover CCU	92		Merseyside Fire Brigade	Command & Control Centre-Derby Rd Liverpool DFS237-Multilift-Leicester Carriage

HFM710X is termed a Heavy Rescue Unit, and was put into service at Warrington by the Cheshire Fire Brigade. It is based on a 1981 Dennis RS133 Water Ladder, and is an example of a pump being re-engineered. Among its varied equipment is a rear - mounted Moffat Mounty fork lift truck. In 1997 Tyne & Wear MFB have done something similar though their example carries a boat.
Clive Shearman

Three Prime Mover appliances were delivered with the white curtain sides to Warwickshire FS one of which, G551XWK, is seen here. Coleshill uses a Foam Tender Pod while an Emergency Tender pod, serves Nuneaton. The pod has since been modified following damage in an accident. The result is that the pod is now level with the height of the cab while the curtain sides are now red. In 1992 Dennis delivered a DFS234 chassis for use as Prime Mover though this time it had a trailing third axle and had a pod with the tank from Bedford TK-HCB Angus PNX999M. *Clive Shearman*

J257KWM	1282	PM /OSU DCU	92		Merseyside Fire Brigade	W1 Exmouth St-Birkenhead DFS237-Multilift-Cocker
J904VRW	PM-4	PMover WRC	92		Warwickshire Fire & Rescue Service	29 Royal Leamington Spa **Tank off Bedford FoT- PNX999M** DFS234-Multilift-Whale Tankers
K945OHF	1291	PM/SRU MRU HLL	93		Merseyside Fire Brigade	C1 Studholme St-Bankhall-Liverpool DFS237-Multilift-Cocker
K946OHF	1292	PMover HLL	93		Merseyside Fire Brigade	E1 Parr Stocks Rd-St Helens DFS237-Multilift-Cocker
L38SFY	1295	PMover BASU	94		Merseyside Fire Brigade	W1 Exmouth St-Birkenhead DFS241-Cargotec-Multilift
L39SFY	1296	PMover	94		Merseyside Fire Brigade	Command & Control-Derby Rd-Liverpool DFS241-Cargotec Multilift
L517XBB	083	FOT	94		Durham Fire & Rescue Service-**1996** Durham County Fire & Rescue Brigade	N1 Watling St-Bishop Auckland SS235-John Dennis CB
M31KPA		DCU	95		Surrey Fire & Rescue Service	21 Gavell Rd-Painshill SS235-John Dennis CB
N143DPX	A00150	Incident C/Unit	96		West Sussex Fire Brigade	20 West Mead's Drive-Bognor Regis Dennis Dart 9SDL-Leicester Carriage Builders
P	A00151	Incident C/Unit	97		West Sussex Fire Brigade	Dennis Dart 9SDL-Leicester Carriage Builders

The Dennis F7 was a very popular pumping appliance in early the Post War years and, in a lot of cases, gave the Firefighters of the period their first taste of riding to a fire enclosed from the elements. Foam Tender FKY719 is the only recorded example of one used as a special. Photographed outside the Nelson Street station in Bradford it operated up until 1974, though it did not make the newly formed West Yorkshire Fire Service. *Ian Moore*

DODGE

Reg No	Fleet No	TYPE	YR	OS	Appliance & Brigade Name	Details/Stations
Types Kew K1050 K850 ; K1113 K2213 G1313/C G1613 G16L/C S50-56C						The early Dodge looked quite similar to the Leyland Comet. It was a 3 ton lorry chassis, powered by a 114 bhp petrol engine. The later K & G series were powered by Perkins or Chrysler engines. Renault who had taken over Dodge in the early 1980's started to show their influence in the late 1980's and the Dodge name disappeared.
Chassis K2213 K1613 G1613 G1617 G16C					**Weight** 22 Tons 16 Tons 16 Tons 16 Tons 16 Tons	The K & G series were powered by Perkins V8 diesel engines. The K chassis was withdrawn in 1980 and replaced by the G series.

Reg No	Fleet No	TYPE	YR	OS	Appliance & Brigade Name	Details/Stations
					Dodge Chassied **Hydraulic Platforms**	
FHY197K		HP	72	90	City of Bristol	#1 Bridewell St-Bristol-1973/#1 Temple Back-Bristol-1974 A1 Temple Back-1978 C1 Milton Ave-Weston super Mare 1987 Reserve-1989 County of Avon/**Sold to Cornwall County FB-1990** K1050-HCB Angus-Simon SS70
GNY886K		HP	72	87	Glamorgan County Fire Brigade (Wales)	Training Centre-1974/Training Centre-1982 W1 Sunnyside-Bridgend-1987 /Mid Glamorgan CFB K1050-Jennings-Simon SS70
GTG179K		HP	72	90	Glamorgan County Fire Brigade (Wales)	C1 Oxford St-Treforrest-Pontypridd-1974 15 Pontypridd-Mid Glamorgan CFB-1990 K1050-Jennings-Simon SS70
FUG500K		PHP	72	89	Leeds City Fire Brigade	Girton Approach-Gipton-1974 /D12 Gipton-1979 F12 Beancroft Rd-Castleford-1989 West Yorkshire FS **Sold to Yorkshire Stone Features-Bradford** K850-Jennings-Simon SS50
JMO115K		PHP	72	83	Berkshire & Reading Fire Brigade	B1 Caversham Rd-Reading-1974 /W1 Caversham Rd-1983 K1050-Carmichael-Orbitor 72'
VCU596L		PHP	72	87	South Shields County Borough FB	Kepple St-South Shields-1974 /K South Shields-1978 Reserve-1987 Tyne & Wear MFB K850-Jennings-Simon SS50
VWR677L		PHP	73	92	West Riding of Yorkshire Fire Brigade	Huddersfield Rd-Dewsbury-1974 C14 Dewsbury-1992/West Yorkshire FS K1050-HCB Angus-Simon SS70
PMR714M		PHP	74	81	Wiltshire Fire Brigade	1/1 Drove Rd-Swindon-1981 **Sold Ballina County Mayo-Republic of Ireland-971XIZ** K850-Merryweather-Simon SS50
RCV273M		HP	74	90	Cornwall County Fire Brigade	A1 Station Rd-Truro **Booms Re-chassied onto Mercedes 1625-Saxon-G284CRL** **Chassis and cab used for Heavy Recovery Vehicle** K1050-HCB Angus-Simon SS220
PSG865M		HP	74	94	South Eastern Area Fire Brigade (Scotland)	**McDonald Rd-Edinburgh-1986**-Res-Lothian & Borders K1050-HCB Angus-Simon SS263

Many of the early Simon hydraulic platforms were mounted on Dodge K850 chassis. Unusual was the Merryweather bodywork on PMR714M, Swindon-based model delivered in 1974. The concept of the Pump/Hydraulic Platform was thought to be the way forward at the time with 'every brigade in the country having one'. As with many of these appliances, they had a relatively short life with their United Kingdom owner, though several went on to further service in the Irish Republic. *Michael Lawmon*

UWX218N		PHP	74	91	West Riding of Yorkshire FB	Bradford Rd-Keighley-1974/A17 Keighley-1980 B11 Skircoat Moor Rd-Halifax-1991 West Yorkshire FS K1050-HCB Angus-Simon SS70
KTF816P		PHP	76	83	Royal Berkshire Fire Brigade	17 Tuns Lane-Slough-1983 **Sold to County Kildare-Newbridge-901ZW** K1613-HCB Angus-Simon SS50
DHW531W	F/59/80	HP	80		County of Avon Fire Brigade-**1996** Avon Fire Brigade	B6 Speedwell Rd-Speedwell-Bristol **RTA Damaged/New cab** G1613-Carmichael-Simon SS220
HSP130W	145	HP	82		Tayside Fire Brigade (Scotland)	A1 Blackness Rd, Dundee - ? A2 Macalpine Rd-Dundee G1613-HCB Angus-Simon SS263
RRN164X		HP	82	92	Lancashire County Fire Brigade	**ex B90 Belvidere Rd-Burnley-1990**/ Reserve-1992 G1613-Angloco-Simon SS220
MTH127X		HP	82		Mid Glamorgan Fire Brigade-**1996** South Wales Fire Service (Wales)	ED 21/21 Dynevor St-Merthyr Tydfil **Booms off ERF 84PS/Jennings-UTX379G -6x2 WD** G1613-Angloco-Simon SS85
A796FDG		HP	83	90	Gloucestershire Fire & Rescue Service	12 Keynsham Rd-Cheltenham **Booms Re-chassied off ERF 84RS-HCB Angus-MDD747F** G16C-Carmichael Simon SS85
A786SUL	HP16	HP	84		GLC London Fire Brigade	**ex H31 Croydon-1990/G39 Faggs Rd-Feltham-London FB** West Area Reserve-Date G16C-Saxon-Simon SS220
A787SUL	HP17	HP	84		GLC London Fire Brigade	**ex B22/H22 Lambeth-1985** **ex B31/H25 West Norwood 1990**/S Area Reserve-Date G16C-Saxon-Simon SS220
B999MSF		HP	84		Fife Fire & Rescue Service (Scotland)	A3 Dunnikeir Rd-Kirkaldy G16L-F&Wylie-Simon SS263
C459RSF		HP	85		Fife Fire & Rescue Service (Scotland)	A1 Carnegie Rd-Dunfermline G16L-F&Wylie-Simon SS263
C433KDS		HP	86		Strathclyde Fire Brigade (Scotland)	D1 Station Rd-Ayr G16L-F&Wylie-Simon SS263
C434AND		HP	86		Greater Manchester County Fire Service	**ex E50 Thompson St-Manchester-1988** B20 Moor Lane-Bolton- G16C-Saxon-Simon SS263

Dodge G16C Turntable Ladder A179DSX was delivered to Dunfermline, in the Kingdom of Fife in 1983. It had the then 'state of the art' Merryweather XRL30 ladders. The XRL ladder was the successor to the 1957 model. This appliance was withdrawn in 1985 after which Fife Fire Brigade went onto purchase Hydraulic Platforms.
Ken Reid

D754EAC	HP4	HP	86		Warwickshire Fire & Rescue Service	ND 20 Newtown Rd-Nuneaton /ex Simon Demonstrator G16C-Saxon-Simon SS263
D683FDE		HP	86		Dyfed Fire Brigade-**1996** Mid & West Wales FB (Wales)	C1/N21 Trefechan-Aberystwyth G16C-Saxon-Simon SS220
D89SCX	004	HP	87		West Yorkshire Fire Service	**ex B Div Bradford-1992**/ A20 Kirkstall Rd-Leeds Central- G16C-Saxon-Simon-SS263
D623DTR		HP	87		Hampshire Fire Service	D54 St Mary's Rd-St Mary's-Southampton **Booms off ERF 84PS- HCB Angus-BCR822K** G16C-Saxon-Simon SS70
D161MWO		HP	87	95	Gwent Fire Brigade (Wales)	B20 Henllys Way-Cwmbran **Booms off ERF 84RS/HCB Angus-JDW976F** G16C-Saxon-Simon SS65
D467BSC		HP	87		Lothian & Borders Fire Brigade (Scotland)	50 Mcdonald Rd-Edingburgh G16C-Saxon-Simon SS263
E379DBL		HP	87		Buckinghamshire Fire & Rescue Service	Cambridge St-Aylesbury **Booms off ERF 84PS/HCB Angus-FBH868K** G16C-Saxon-Simon SS70
E360KHY		HP	87		Fire Service College	Moreton in Marsh-Gloucestershire G16C-Saxon-Simon SS220
E741HRV		HP	87	96	Hampshire Fire & Rescue Service	B17 Station Approach-Fareham-1995/ **Unallocated** **Booms off ERF 84PS/ HCB Angus-GOR70K** G16C-Saxon-Simon SS70
E777WBU		HP	88		Greater Manchester County Fire Service	**ex E50 Thompson St-Manchester-1996**/ Reserve- G16C-Saxon-Simon SS263
F516WVP	117	HP	88		West Midlands Fire Service	**ex C4 Bournbrook-1992**/B3 Radford Rd-Coventry- Renault G16C-Gloster Saro-Simon SS263
F994NRV		HP	88	96	Hampshire Fire & Rescue Service	A01 West Ham Close-Basingstoke **Booms off ERF 84PS/ HCB Angus-FCG70K** Renault G17C-Saxon-Simon SS70

JMO115K was photographed at Caversham Road station in Reading and is a Dodge K1050 Hydraulic Platform. Delivered in 1972 from Carmichael, it had the more unusual 72 foot Orbitor booms which were rare in this country - only eight seeing service. The other examples at the Cities of Belfast, Bradford (2) County Boroughs of St Helens and Bootle, South Western Area (Scotland) and Merthyr Tydfil UDC with all major chassis types having a share of the market.
David Thomas

E709GFE (later F576HTL)		HP	88		Lincolnshire Fire & Rescue Service	A1 South Park Ave-Lincoln Renault G16C-Saxon-Simon SS263
F674GNC		HP	89		Greater Manchester County Fire Service	D44 Denhill Rd-Moss Side Renault G16C-Saxon-Simon SS263
G662TFW		HP	89		Lincolnshire Fire & Rescue Service	C1 Robin Hoods Walk-Boston Renault G16C-Saxon-Simon SS263
G199SRJ		HP	90		Greater Manchester County Fire Service	C33 Lees Rd-Oldham Renault G16C-Saxon-Simon SS263
G186UPO		HP	90		Hampshire Fire & Rescue Service	A02 Lynchford Rd-Rushmoor -1996/ **Unallocated** **Booms off Leyland Beaver HCB Angus-GPX70N** Renault G17C-Angloco-Simon SS70

					Dodge Chassied Turntable Ladders	
JFS406N		TL	75	91	Lothian & Borders Fire Brigade (Scotland)	51 Telford Rd-Crewe Toll-Edinburgh 1991 K2213-Carmichael-Magirus
MFS27P		TL	76	95	Lothian & Borders Fire Brigade (Scotland)	**ex 30 Ponton St-Toll Cross-Edinburgh-1990**/Reserve-Date K2213-Carmichael-Magirus
RWW266R		TL	76	90	West Yorkshire Fire Service	D11 Kirkstall Rd-Leeds-1989/Reserve-1990 K1613-Carmichael-Magirus
RHW384S		TL	78	96	County of Avon Fire Brigade	C5 Hartcliffe Way-Bedminster G1613-Carmichael-Magirus DLK30
RHW385S		TL	78	94	County of Avon Fire Brigade	**ex A1 Temple Back-Temple-1986** C1 Milton Ave-West super Mare/**Written off in RTA** G1613-Carmichael-Magirus DLK30
XMW758T		TL	79		Wiltshire Fire Brigade	**ex 1/1 Drove Rd-Swindon-1993** /Reserve-Date G16C-Carmichael-Magirus DL30
LNF92V		TL	80	95	Greater Manchester County Fire Service	**ex A10 The Crescent-Salford-1983** **ex A13 Liverpool Rd-Eccles-1985** /Reserve-Date G16C-Carmichael-Magirus DL30
LNF93V		TL	80	95	Greater Manchester County Fire Service	**ex B27 Windermere Rd-Leigh-1989** **ex B27 St Helens Rd-Leigh-1993**/Reserve-Date G16C-Carmichael-Magirus DL30
LNF94V		TL	80	95	Greater Manchester County Fire Service	**ex C36 The Rock-Bury-1987** **ex D40 Whitehill St-Stockport-1993** /Reserve-1995 **GB Fire UK Loan Vehicle -** Lothian & Borders FB G16C-Carmichael-Magirus DL30
LNF95V		TL	80	?	Greater Manchester County Fire Service	? G16C-Carmichael-Magirus DL30
LHH678W		TL	81	88	Cumbria Fire Service	Warwick St-Carlisle-1988 **Ladders Re-chassied off Commer-Haydon-BHH385B** G1613-Carmichael-Magirus DL30
YSM430W		TL	81	96	Dumfries & Galloway Fire Brigade (Scotland)	**ex D1 Dumfries-1990** /Reserve-Date **Ladders Re chassied off Commer USD443** G1613-Carmichael-Magirus DL-30
GFR598W	30108	TL	81		Lancashire County Fire Brigade	**ex 37 South Shore-Blackpool-1984** /Reserve-Date G1617-Carmichael-Magirus DL30U
NCK935X	30109	TL	81		Lancashire County Fire Brigade	A12 Clark St-Morecombe G1617-Carmichael-Magirus DL30U
SHH26X		TL	82	88	Cumbria Fire Service	Abbey Rd-Barrow in Furness-1988 **L off Dennis F107-BEO864C-Barrow in Furness CB** G1613-Carmichael-Magirus
TDA441Y		TL	83	96	Gloucestershire Fire & Rescue Service	**05 Eastern Ave-Gloucester-1988**/GPV-12 Cheltenham-1996 **Ladders removed from chassis and sold abroad** G13C-Carmichael-Riffaud EPA24-80'

BNB707Y		TL	82	96	Greater Manchester County Fire Service	E54 Hodgeson St-Ashton under Lyne /**Damaged in RTA** G16C-Carmichael-Magirus-DL30U
BNB708Y		TL	82	95	Greater Manchester County Fire Service	**ex A10 Salford-1992**/Reserve-Date G16C-Carmichael-Magirus-DL30U
NYV790Y	TL40P	TLP	83		GLC London Fire Brigade	**ex C24/F33 Whitechapel-1990/ex A21 Paddington-1993** North Area-Reserve G16C-Carmichael-Magirus DL30U
NYV791Y	TL41P	TLP	83		GLC London Fire Brigade	**ex B31/H25 West Norwood-1990/** West Area-Reserve- G16C-Carmichael-Magirus DL30U
A179DSX		TL	83	85	Fife Fire Brigade (Scotland)	A1 Carnegie Road, Dunfermline **This machine was withdrawn** G16C-Merryweather-XRL30-100'L
A929JBU		TL	83	96	Greater Manchester County Fire Service	C36 The Rock-Bury-1996/ **Crack found in a ladder section** G1617-Carmichael-Magirus DL30E
A792SUL	TL42P	TLP	83		GLC London Fire Brigade	**ex D27/G38 Heston-1990/NE Res-1995**/A30 Islington- G16C-Carmichael-Magirus DL30E
A793SUL	TL43P	TLP	83		GLC London Fire Brigade	**ex B21/H21 Clapham-1990/North Training-1995**/WDR- G16C-Carmichael-Magirus DL30E
A794SUL	TL44P	TLP	83		GLC London Fire Brigade	**ex A24 Soho-1988 /ex A28 Dowgate-1992 ex A42 Lancaster Grove-Belsize-1995**/ East Reserve-Date G16C-Carmichael-Magirus DL30E
A914KJC		TL	84		Gwynedd Fire Service -**1996** North Wales Fire Service (Wales)	03/C01 Conway Rd-Llandudno G16C-Carmichael-Magirus DL30E
B730BYS		TL	84	?	Strathclyde Fire Brigade (Scotland)	B2 Goven - ? - **Withdrawn** G16C-Merryweather-XRL30-100'L
B545WYO	TL45P	TLP	84		GLC London Fire Brigade	**ex B22/H22 Lambeth-1991/ H31Old Town Croydon-1995** South Reserve-Date G16C-Carmichael-Magirus-DL30U
B546WYO	TL46P	TLP	84		GLC London Fire Brigade	**ex H21/E39 Bromley-1991**/E35/B35 Old Kent Road- G16C-Carmichael-Magirus DL30U
B547WYO	TL47P	TLP	84		GLC London Fire Brigade	**South East Training -1995**/B21/H21 High St-Clapham- G16C-Carmichael-Magirus DL30U
B457BHB		TL	84		South Glamorgan Fire Service-**1996** South Wales Fire Service (Wales)	01 Adam St-Cardiff G16C-Angloco-Metz DLK30
B157USR		TL	85	92	Tayside Fire Brigade (Scotland)	A2 Strathmore Ave-Dundee **Ladders Re-chassied off AEC Mercury-LES448** G16C-G&T Power-Merryweather
C773OCW	30007	TL	85		Lancashire County Fire Brigade	**ex AD37 South Shore-Blackpool-1992** AD31 Redbank Rd-Bispham-Blackpool G16C-Angloco-Metz DLK30
C859GCX	007	TL	86		West Yorkshire Fire Service	**ex CD Lister St-Brighouse-Leeds-1995**/ D Reserve- G16C-Carmichael-Magirus DL30E
C860GCX	008	TL	86		West Yorkshire Fire Service	**ex CD Outcote Bank-Huddersfield-1995**/ C Reserve- G16C-Carmichael-Magirus DL30E
C310JEP		TL	86	90	West Glamorgan County Fire Service (Wales)	5 Grove Place-Swansea-1990 **Ladders Re-ch onto Scania G93M-Angloco-G429KBO** G1613-Angloco-Metz
C779VGV		TL	86	90	Suffolk Fire Service	A02 Princes St-Ipswich /**Written off in RTA -1990 Ladder Re-ch onto Mercedes 1726-Carmichael J990SOL** G16C-Carmichael-Magirus
E999BRB	TU-09	TL	88		Derbyshire Fire Service	C1 Sheffield Rd-Chesterfield G16C-Carmichael-Magirus DL30E
E199XJC		TL	88		Gwynedd Fire Service-**1996** North Wales Fire Service (Wales)	01/W02 Beach Rd-Bangor Renault G16C-Carmichael-Magirus DL30E
G39DSF		TL	90		Lothian & Borders Fire Brigade (Scotland)	30 Ponton St-Toll Cross Edinghurg Renault G16C-Carmichael-Magirus DL30E

EMS262V is an Emergency Support Unit which was based at Rosyth in Fife and is based in a 1980 Dodge G1313, similar to that used for the pump appliance market. In this example Fulton & Wylie carried out the conversion work as the unit used the body off the Bedford TK Emergency Tender MFG298G which also served at Rosyth. A sister appliance served at Lochgelly as an Emergency Tender but has now been transfered to other duties. *Ken Reid*

					Dodge Chassied Emergency/Rescue Tenders	
TES268K		Res/T	72	92	Perth & Kinross Fire Brigade (Scotland)	**ex Water Escape-Crieff** **Converted to Emergency Tender-1992** A11 Kingsway-Tayside FB K850-HCB Angus
GTG642K		Rec/V	71	87	Berkshire & Reading Fire Brigade	B22 Dee Rd-Reading-1977 W2 Wokingham Rd-Reading-1987 K1050-Bates Holmes
PMR713M		Res/T	73	90	Wiltshire Fire Brigade	1/1 Drove Rd-Swindon-1990 **Converted to Damage Control Unit -Date** K850-Merryweather
GHR618N		Res/T	74	90	Wiltshire Fire Brigade	3/1 Ashley Rd-Sailsbury-1990 **Converted to Damage Control Unit -Date** K850-Merryweather
SVF795N		ET	74	95	Norfolk Fire Brigade	C69 Friars Lane-Great Yarmouth-1979 **Conv Chemical Incident Unit**/A29 Chartwell Rd-Sprowston K850-HCB Angus/NFB
HOX355N	249	ET/CU	75	86	West Midlands Fire Service	E5 Merridale St-Wolverhampton K850-Benson
NPW29P		Res/T	76		Norfolk Fire Service	**ex WRL**/ 44 Norwich Rd-Fakenham K850-HCB Angus-NFS
ONK198P		ET	76	92	Buckinghamshire Fire Brigade	B1 Cambridge St-Aylesbury-1988 K1113-ERF Firefighter
KTC601P		MRT	76	90	County of Avon Fire Brigade	A5 Rodway Rd-Patchway-Bristol K1613-Wreckers International
UCL165R		Res/T	77	92	Norfolk Fire Service	**ex WRL**/ 54 Norwich Rd-Thetford-1992 K1113-ERF-NFS

PMR713M is seen here in 1993 oustide the Drove Road fire station in Swindon. By then this Damage Control Unit , based on a Dodge K850, had ceased to be used as an Emergency Tender of which two were delivered to the Wiltshire Fire Brigade in the early 1970s. PMR713M was delivered in 1973, while GHR618N went to Ashley Road in   Sailsbury in 1974, and   that example, too, is also on Damage

Reg	Fleet No	Type	Year	Decommissioned	Brigade	Details
SPP514R		ET	77	93	Buckinghamshire Fire Brigade	C1 St Marys St-High Wycombe-1988 **HGV Vehicle** K1113-ERF Firefighter
SGS863R		Res/T	77	93	Hertfordshire County Fire Brigade	**ex Water Ladder**-Cheshunt-1983 Converted to Rescue Tender-Reserve K1113-HCB Angus
WBA545S		E/ST	77	94	Greater Manchester County Fire Service	A13 Liverpool Rd-Eccles-1985 Reserve-1994 K1113-Eagle
WBA546S		E/ST	77	94	Greater Manchester County Fire Service	D42 Lisburne Lane-Offerton-1984 Reserve-1994 K1113-Eagle
RHW386S		Res/T	77	93	County of Avon Fire Brigade	A1 Temple Back-Temple-Bristol-1989-Reserve-1993 K1113-HCB Angus
THO981T		Res/T	79	94	Hampshire Fire Brigade	C30 North Walls-Winchester-1994 Power Wagon-HCB Angus
THO982T		Res/T	79	95	Hampshire Fire Brigade	D48 Southampton Rd-Lyndhurst-1995 Power Wagon-HCB Angus
THO983T		Res/T	79	92	Hampshire Fire Brigade	A1 West Ham Close-Basingstoke-1984 C31 London Rd-Andover-1992 Power Wagon-HCB Angus
PCG972T		Res/T	79	90	Fife Fire Brigade (Scotland)	A6 Castle Rd-Rosyth- Reserve-1990-**ex Doemonstrator** Power Wagon-HCB Angus
NNM826V		ET	80	92	Buckinghamshire Fire Brigade	A1 Sherwood Drive-Bletchley-1987 **Converted to Operational Support Unit** 6.1 Skelton Close-Beaconsfield-1992 G1313-Angloco
VDR291V	5243	ET	80		Devon Fire & Rescue Service	**50 Greenbank Rd-Plymouth-1995**/49 Crownhill-Plymouth-G1213-Benson
VDR292V	5244	ET	80		Devon Fire & Rescue Service	32 Howells Rd-Exeter-G1213-Benson

In the 1980s, the Renault-Dodge S56 was popular as a medium sized chassis with many brigades. Carmichael-bodied Rescue Tender A195LDG was pictured at its Keynsham Road, Cheltenham base in 1989. The appliance replaced a Ford D Series fitted with a crane, (which possibly suited the role better) as the Dodge was itself replaced with a larger unit, an Emergency Tender based on a Mercedes 1120AF with Locomotors body, using a HIAB 071 crane.
Clive Shearman

Reg		Type			Brigade	Details
BLS743V		ET	80		Fife Fire Brigade (Scotland)	A4 Lumphinnans Rd -Lochgelly-1991 **Converted Breathing Apparatus Tender-Date** G1313-Fulton & Wylie
EMS262V		ESU	80		Fife Fire & Rescue Service (Scotland)	**ex A6 Castle Rd-Rosyth-1996**/ Reserve **Body from Bedford TKEL-MFG298G** G1313-Methven & Thomson-F&W
AHU388V	F/63/80 F/66/85	Res/T	80		County of Avon Fire Brigade-**1996** Avon Fire Brigade	exC1 Weston super Mare -1993 Reserve/**Conv GP Lorry** G1213-Cheshire FE
NNC18W		ET Salv/T	81	94	Greater Manchester County Fire Service	D42 Lisburne Lane-Offerton-Stockport G1313-Angloco
NNC19W		ET Salv/T	81	95	Greater Manchester County Fire Service	ex C30 Rochdale-1992 /Reserve G1313-Angloco
BTP484W		Res/T	81	95	Hampshire Fire Brigade	B17 Station Approach-Fareham-1995 Power Wagon-HCB Angus
BTP485W		Res/T	81		Hampshire Fire Brigade	C31 London Rd-Andover-1984 A1 West Ham Close-Basingstoke-1986 C29 Steele Close-Eastleigh-1990 Power Wagon-HCB Angus
BTP486W		Res/T	81	90	Hampshire Fire Brigade	A2 Ordanance Rd-Aldershot / A2 Rushmoor-1990 Power Wagon-HCB Angus
FHR622W		Res/T	81	95	Wiltshire Fire Brigade	4/1 Hilperton Rd-Trowbridge-1993 Reserve-Date S56C-Carmichael
JHB864W		Res/T	81	87	Gwent Fire Brigade (Wales)	B05 Cemetery Rd-Ebbw Vale-1986 S56C-Pilcher Green
JHB865W		Res/T	81	95	Gwent Fire Brigade (Wales)	B09 Malpas Rd-Newport-1986 **Converted Towing Unit-Date** S56C-Pilcher Green
FSP923W		ET	81		Tayside Fire Brigade (Scotland)	ex WRL-1992/ Reserve G1313-HCB Angus-TFB
MKG37X		Res/T	82	91	South Glamorgan County FB (Wales)	1 Adam St-Cardiff-1991 S66C-Angloco
TTV953X		Res/T	82	94	Nottinghamshire Fire Brigade	B18 Shakespeare St-Nottingham-1987 Reserve-Date S66C-Fulton & Wylie
JHY616X		Res/T	82	89	Gloucestershire Fire & Rescue Service	07 Paganhill Lane-Stroud S66C-Carmichael
VUT311X		ETCU	82		Leicestershire Fire & Rescue Service	N20 Epinal Way-Loughborough G1313-Angloco
VUT312X		ETCU	82		Leicestershire Fire & Rescue Service	S30 Lancaster Rd-Leicester-1995/40 Leicester Southern- G1313-Angloco
BRY103Y		Res/T	82		Leicestershire Fire & Rescue Service	S38 Leicester Rd-Hinckley S66C-HCB Angus
BRY104Y		Res/T	82		Leicestershire Fire & Rescue Service	S33 South St-Oakham S66C-HCB Angus
NSX359Y		ET	82	92	Lothian & Borders Fire Borders (Scotland)	50 Macdonald Rd-Edinburgh **Damaged in RTA** S66C-Mountain Range
STX537Y		Res/T	83	94	South Glamorgan Fire Service (Wales)	ex 5 Barry-1992 /B18 Wimborne Rd-Poole-1994 Dorset Fire Brigade S56C-Merryweather-DFB
PCY814Y		Res/T	83		West Glamorgan County FS-**1996** Mid & West Wales FB-(Wales)	ex 8 Snay Rd-Morriston-1989/ Reserve- S56C-Angloco
A84XUX		ET	83	95	Shropshire Fire & Rescue Service	ex B Div Wellington-1991 /B Div Stafford Park-Telford G13C-Saxon
A261JMS		SSU	83		Central Region Fire Brigade-**1996** Central Scotland FB(Scotland)	F3 Grangemouth Rd-Falkirk- G75C-F&Wylie
A195LDG		Res/T	84	93	Gloucestershire Fire & Rescue Service	12 Keynsham Rd-Cheltenham S56C-Carmichael
A451LND		ET	84		Lothian & Borders Fire Brigade (Scotland)	54 Glasgow Rd-Bathgate - relocated to 54 Boghall S66C-Mountain Range

A974NDV	5047	ET	84		Devon Fire & Rescue Service	01 North Rd-Barnstaple G12C-Angloco
A975NDV	5048	ET	84		Devon Fire & Rescue Service	17 Newton Rd-Torquay G12C-Angloco
A92EAO	05-03	Res/T	84		Cumbria Fire Service	B Div Abbey Rd-Barrow in Furness G12C-Ecrolite
A695MNC		ET Salv/T	84	95	Greater Manchester County Fire Service	E53 Birch St-Gorton-Manchester G13C-Mountain Range
A696MNC		ET Salv/T	84	95	Greater Manchester County Fire Service	B24 Robin Park Rd-Wigan G13C-Mountain Range
A737MDB		ET	84	95	County of Clwyd Fire Brigade (Wales)	E1 Bradley Rd-Wrexham S66C-F&Wylie
A284NRO		ET	84	93	Buckinghamshire Fire Brigade	C3 Tatling End-Oxford Rd-Gerrards Cross-1987 **Converted to Operational Support Unit** 2.1 Sherwood Drive-Bletchley-1993 G13C-Saxon
B441VAE	F/67/84	Res/T	84		County of Avon Fire Brigade-**1996** Avon Fire Brigade	**ex B1 Cleveland Bridge-Bath-1989** A1 Temple Back-Temple-Bristol- G13C-Carmichael
B414WES		ET	85	86	Tayside Fire Brigade (Scotland)	B1 High St-Perth-**Written off in RTA** G13C-Tayside FB
B284OEY		ET	85		County of Clwyd Fire Brigade-**1996** North Wales Fire Service (Wales)	W2 Abergale Rd-Colwyn Bay-1995/Reserve- S66C-Mountain Range
B645UDB		ET Salv/T	85	95	Greater Manchester County Fire Service	A13 Liverpool Rd-Eccles G13C-Mountain Range
B652HRM	05-04	Res/T	85		Cumbria Fire Service	**ex C Div Warwick St-Carlisle-1996**/ Reserve- G12C-Ecrolite
B713KRM	05-05	Res/T	85		Cumbria Fire Service	C Div Bridge St-Penrith G12C-Ecrolite
B998KSO		Res/U	85	97	Grampian Fire Brigade (Scotland)	N77 North Anderson Drive-Aberdeen G10C-Mountain Range
B999KSO		Res/U	85	97	Grampian Fire Brigade (Scotland)	N70 Dennyduff Rd-Fraserburgh G10C-Mountain Range
D234ESR		ET	86		Tayside Fire Brigade (Scotland)	A2 Macalpine Rd-Dundee G13C-Tayside FB
D637ESL		ET	86		Tayside Fire Brigade (Scotland)	B1 High St-Perth G13C-Tayside FB
D426TAO	05-06	Res/T	87		Cumbria Fire Service	B Div Busher Walk-Kendal G12C-Ecrolite
D539TRM	06-01	SIU	87		Cumbria Fire Service	B Div Busher Walk-Kendal G11C-Robin Hood
D540TRM	06-02	SIU	87		Cumbria Fire Service	A Div Hensingham-Whitahaven G11C-Robin Hood
E999YRC		Res/T	87		Nottinghamshire Fire & Rescue Service	**ex 18 Central-1993**/ 21 Abbey Rd-Dunkirk-Nottingham **Damaged in RTA-1996** G13C-FSE Leicestershire
E496UKF	1243	ET/CU	87		Merseyside Fire Brigade	**ex C1 Studholme St-Bankhall-1991**/ Reserve- G13C-Carmichael
E799BTN	221	ET	87	93	Durham County Fire Brigade	C1 Woodstone Villages-Fencehouses Renault S56C-Custom Line
F988KVK	225	ET	88	95	Durham County Fire Brigade	E1 Surtees Rd-Peterlee Renault S56C-Devco Plan
F434GSA		ET	88	97	Grampian Fire Brigade (Scotland)	N37 Friars Rd-Elgin Renault G10C-Mountain Range
F990GRC		Res/T	88		Nottinghamshire Fire & Rescue Service	12 Wharf Rd-Retford Renault G13TC-Carmichael
F999GRC		Res/T	88		Nottinghamshire Fire & Rescue Service	16 Boundary Rd-Newark Renault G13TC-Carmichael

F855SHD	114	ET	89		West Yorkshire Fire Service	D Div Brunswick St-Wakefield Renault G08C-Devcoplan
F280PFF		ET	89		Gwynedd Fire Service-**1996** North Wales Fire Service (Wales)	09/W01 Llanberis-Caernarfon Renault G12C-Carmichael
L445MNN		Res/T	93		Nottinghamshire Fire & Rescue Service	05 Sutton Rd-Kirkby in Ashfield Renault M230 Midliner-Carmichael International
M551TET	ET-01	Res/T	95		Derbyshire Fire Service	B01 Campton Grove-Buxton Renault M230 Midliner-Angloco
M552TET	ET-02	Res/T	95		Derbyshire Fire Service	A03 Derby Rd-Ripley Renault M230 Midliner-Angloco
N603NHY	F/63/96	Res/T	96		Avon Fire Brigade	A01-Temple Back-Temple-Bristol Renault M230 Midliner-Saxon-**Hiab 071**

					Dodge Chassied **Specialist Appliances**	
92F		FoT	57	71	Essex County Fire Brigade	Hogg Lane-Grays Kew-Sun
812LNO	FT-4	FoT	58	73	Essex County Fire Brigade	Rainham Rd-Dagenham-1965/L27 Alfreds Way-Barking- 1971 L21 High St-East Ham-1973 /London Fire Brigade Kew-Sun
XRH448J		Artic Foam Trailer	71	80	City of Kingston upon Hull Fire Brigade	#4 Clough Rd-Hull North-1974 A2 Clough Rd-Hull North-1980/Humberside Fire Brigade **K Series Tractor Unit-Class 1 HGV**
CAE856J		FoT	71	85	City of Bristol Fire Brigade	#3 St Andrews Rd-Avonmouth-1974 A3 Avonmouth-1985 /County of Avon K1050-Carmichael
GTX600K		PMover DCU	72	90	County Fire Service (Wales)	**ex WRL 07 Reynoldston**/04 Commercial Rd-Port Talbot K850-HCB Angus-WGFB
GTG642K	S6	Rec/V	72	86	Berkshire & Reading Fire Brigade	02 Wokingham Rd-Reading-1974/02Wokingham Rd-1977 03 Dee Rd-Reading-1982/01 Caversham Rd-Reading-1986 Royal Berkshire Fire & Rescue Service K1050-Bates Holmes
BMS703L		FOT	72	85	Central Area Fire Brigade (Scotland)	Grangemouth Rd-Falkirk-1975 F3 Grangemouth Rd- Falkirk-1981 - Bowness Fire Station - 1985 - Central Region FB K1050-HCB Angus
ULF743M		Salv/T	74	80	London Salvage Corps	Aldersgate-London/**Preserved** K850-HCB Angus
RCV273M		Rec/V	74		Cornwall County Fire Brigade	**ex HP-Truro-1990** /Brigade Workshops K1050-HCB Angus/Dennis/CCFB
PYG769M		F/Salv	74	85	West Riding of Yorkshire	Beancroft Rd-Castleford-1974 F12 Castleford-1985 /West Yorkshire Fire Service K850-WRYFB
PMR713M		DCU	74		Wiltshire Fire Brigade	**ex ET 1/1 Swindon-1990** -1/1 Drove Rd-Swindon K850-Merryweather-WFB
GHR618N		DCU	74		Wiltshire Fire Brigade	**ex ET 3/1-Sailsbury-1990**-4/4 Meadow Lane Westbury K850-Merryweather-WFB
SVF795N		CIU	74	96	Norfolk Fire Brigade	**ex ET C69 Great Yarmouth-1979** A29 Chartwell Rd-Sprowston Norwich-Date K850/HCB Angus/Norfolk FB
MSR516P		F/SalvT	76		Tayside Fire Brigade (Scotland)	**ex WRL Kingsway East-Dundee**/A4 Ponderlaw St- Arbroath K1113-HCB Angus/TFB
KTX595P		PMover FOC	76	95	Gwent Fire Brigade (Wales)	B10 Lighthouse Rd-Duffryn K850-Bostock Barshy-Carmichael
LOW465R		Rec/V	76		Hampshire Fire Service	**ex Simoniter TSM15** **D58 Falconer Court-Fawley-1984**/Fire Brigade Workshops K1316-Wreckers International
MMR600R		PMover	77		Wiltshire Fire Brigade	**ex HGV Training** / 3/1 Ashley Rd-Sailsbury K1113-Jones Bence

Reg	Fleet	Type	Yr	Yr2	Brigade	Notes
CSC591S	A54	F/Salv	78		Fife Fire Brigade (Scotland)	**ex WRL-1984** /A5 Methilhaven Rd-Methil K1113-HCB Angus/FFB
CSC592S		Rec/V	78		Fife Fire Brigade (Scotland)	**ex WRL-1983**/Brigade Workshops-1988 K1113-HCB Angus/FFB
XRO614S		Fot/Wrc	78		Bedfordshire Fire Brigade	12 Southfields Rd-Kempston-1992 **Sold to Lincolnshire F&RS / C2 West Elloe Ave-Spalding** K1613-Anglo
XRO615S		Fot/Wrc	78		Bedfordshire Fire Brigade	10 Dunstable Rd-Toddington-1992 **Tank sold to Oxfordshire F&RS** K1613-Anglo
AUH289T		FOT	78	96	South Glamorgan Fire Service (Wales)	1 Adam St Central-Cardiff K850-HCB Angus
BDW410T		FOT	78	96	South Glamorgan Fire Service (Wales)	5 Port Rd West-Barry K850-HCB Angus
AND406T		PMover	78		Greater Manchester County Fire Service	A17 Newby Drive-Altrincham **Articulated Unit-Operational Support Unit** B20 Moor Lane-Bolton -**Canteen Unit** G1811P-
AND409T		PMover	78		Greater Manchester County Fire Service	B20 Moor Lane-Bolton /**Articulated Unit-Canteen Unit** G1811P-
XWO535T		PMover	78	91	South Glamorgan Fire Service (Wales)	1 Adam St-Cardiff G1313-Powell Duffryn
XLS278T		FSU	79		Central Region Fire Brigade-**1996** Central Scotland FB (Scotland)	**ex WRL- ? / F1** Linlithgow Rd-Bowness G1314-F&Wylie
GNF709V		PMover	79		Greater Manchester County Fire Service	E51 Rochdale Rd-Blackley **Articulated Unit-Damage Control** G1811P-
BTN47V	310	PMover	80		Tyne & Wear Metropolitan Fire Brigade	Tyne & Wear Station's G7575-David Earl-NE Coachbuilder's
BTN48V	317	PMover	80		Tyne & Wear Metropolitan Fire Brigade	Tyne & Wear Station's G7575-David Earl-NE Coachbuilder's
TTJ317V	1193	CAV	80	95	Merseyside Fire Brigade	W1 Exmouth St-Birkenhead S56C-Cocker
CYH441V		FOT	80		Fire Service College	Moreton in Marsh-Gloucestershire **This appliance was involved in a fatal RTA when it rolled over on one of the runways during testing.** G13C-Carmichael
PNB480W		PMover	80		Greater Manchester County Fire Service	A12 Bolton Rd-Agecroft/**Articulated Unit-Control Unit** G1811P-
MRB731W		FOT Salv/T	80	96	Derbyshire Fire Service	C01 Sheffield Rd-Chesterfield G1313-Derby Comercials
MRB732W		FOT Salv/T	80	96	Derbyshire Fire Service	A02 Tamworth Rd-Long Eaton G1313-Derby Comercials
JHB865W		PM /CAU FPU	81	95	Gwent Fire Brigade (Wales)	**ex Res/T B09 Malpas-Newport-1986** B09 Malpas Rd-Malpas-Newport/**Articulated Unit** S56-Pilcher Green-Lynton
YAB257W		C/Unit	81		Hereford & Worcester Fire Brigade	**ex 26 Droitwich-1991** **ex 21 Copenhagen St-Worcester-1994** 41 Worcester Rd-Malvern G1313-Benson
FSP924W		C/Unit	81		Tayside Fire Brigade (Scotland)	**ex WRL**/A1 Blackness Rd-Dundee G1313-HCB Angus-TFB
ATU291W		CAV	81		County of Clwyd Fire Service-**1996** North Wales Fire Service (Wales)	E2/E02 Chester Rd-Queensferry-Deeside S35C-Besco
KKY939W		PM/DCU Salv/T	81	95	South Yorkshire County Fire Service	20 Knolbeck Lane-Brampton Bierlow G13C-Rolonoff
OVO83W	WC-03	WRC	82		Derbyshire Fire Service	A01 Derby Rd-Ilkeston G1613-Angloco-Butterfield
HSP134W		FOT Salv/T	82		Tayside Fire Brigade (Scotland)	**ex WRT**/A11 Kingsway East-Dundee G1313-HCB Angus-TFB

LBX805X		Foam Eqp Unit	**82** 86		Dyfed Fire Brigade-**1996** Mid & West Wales Fire Service	**ex Esso Tanker- ?** / B2/W12 Yorke St Milford Haven G7575- Cheshire FE-DFB
PHE653X		PMover WRC	82	95	South Yorkshire County Fire Service	20 Knolbeck Lane-Brampton Bierlow G13C-Rolonoff
HSG741X		FOT Salv/T	82		Lothian & Borders Fire Brigade (Scotland)	52 Marionville Rd-Marionville Edingburgh G1313-Penman
PRC531X		BAT	82	96	Derbyshire Fire Service	**ex C1 Chesterfield-1986**/A02 Tamworth Rd-Long Eaton G08C-DFS
NDW220X		FOT	82		Mid Glamorgan Fire Brigade-**1996** South Wales Fire Service (Wales)	**ex WRL 21 Merthyr Tydfil** /ED 24 Waunfach St-Caerphilly G1313-CFE-MGFB
NDW221X		FOT	82		Mid Glamorgan Fire Brigade-**1996** South Wales Fire Service (Wales)	**ex WRL 21 Merthyr Tydfil**/WD 01 Angel St-Bridgend G1313-CFE-MGFB
NAM362X		C/Unit	82		Wiltshire Fire Brigade	2/1 Dallas Rd-Chippenham G09-Benson
WJT651X		C/Unit	82		Dorset Fire Brigade	B17 Blandford Rd-Hamworthy S56C-Coversgate
GYM716W KUV747X NYV788Y PJD919/23Y A809-815TYO D866-870FYM F641OYL	HDC-1- 21	HDC PMover	82-89		London Fire Brigade	**In 1982 the London Fire Brigade started purchasing a prime mover pod system. The movements of these machines is far to extensive to enter into. They were designated Heavy De mountable Chassis.** G13C-Wadhams-Locomotors-Arlington
ALY911Y		Salv/T	82		London Salvage Corps	**ex Aldersgate-London-1985** Fire Service College-Moreton in Marsh Gloucestershire G13C-HCB Angus
ARY453Y		FOT Salv/T	82		Leicestershire Fire Service	**ex SD30 Central-1992** SD 31 Bull Head St-Wigston G13C-Carmichael
ARY454Y		FOT Salv/T	82		Leicestershire Fire Service	**ex ND 2- Loughborough-1992** ND25 Broad St-Coalville G13C-Carmichael
CDG998Y		CIU	82	93	Gloucestershire Fire & Rescue Service	07 Pagen Hill Lane-Stroud G75C-Carmichael

Dodge G1181 tractor cab PNB480W was one of four which served the Greater Manchester CFS towing Articulated Unit's. This Canteen Unit, the only example still in operation, served out of Moor Lane in Bolton when photographed in 1993. The other units were Operational Support at Altrincham, Damage Control at Blackley and Control Unit at Agecroft.
Clive Shearman

WSE290Y		PM CAV C/ Unit Hi ex FU	83		Grampian Fire Brigade (Scotland)	E77 North Anderson Drive-Aberdeen G1313-Multilift
UKW386Y		CAV	83		South Yorkshire County Fire Service	Brigade Headquarters G10C-Wilson
PVK889Y	339	PMover	83		Tyne & Wear Metropolitan Fire Brigade	Tyne & Wear Station's G08C-David Earl-Depenbable
A197GUT		CIU	84		Leicestershire Fire Service	SD30 Lancaster Rd-Leicester G10C-Benson
A958ONB		FOT	84		Greater Manchester County Fire Service	A16 Cranleigh Ave-Sale G16C-Carmichael
A108NEL		FOC	84		Dorset Fire Brigade	B18 Wimborne Rd-Poole S50C-Locomotors
A533GMS		P Mover DCU	84		Lothian & Borders Fire Brigade (Scotland)	A1 McDonald Road, Edinburgh G13C
A209HFH	605	PMover	84	95	Gloucestershire Fire & Rescue Service	ex WRL 01 Lydney/Reserve RG13C-Carmichael/Watts
A210HFH	606	PMover C/Unit	84		Gloucestershire Fire & Rescue Service	ex WRL 08 Nailsworth 05 Eastern Ave-Gloucester RG13C-Carmichael/Watts
A194LDG	610	PMover DCU	84		Gloucestershire Fire & Rescue Service	ex WRL 20 Fairford/12 Keynsham Rd-Cheltenham RG13C-Carmichael/Watts
B183SDF	630	PMover ISU	84		Gloucestershire Fire & Rescue Service	ex WRL 02 Coleford /21 Chesterton Lane-Cirencester RG13C-Carmichael/Watts
B184SDF	631	PMover Fire Safety	84		Gloucestershire Fire & Rescue Service	ex WRL 10 Dursley /Reserve RG13C-Carmichael/Watts
B157USR		PMover	84	94	Tayside Fire Brigade (Scotland)	ex TL A2 Dundee-1991/B1 High St-Perth G16C-TFB
B449VAE		PMover FOT	85	92	County of Avon Fire Brigade	A3 St Andrews Rd-Avonmouth G13C-Saxon-Bracey
B450VAE		PMover FOT	85	92	County of Avon Fire Brigade	A3 St Andrews Rd-Avonmouth G13C-Saxon-Bracey
B731AKG		DCU	85		South Glamorgan Fire Service-**1996** South Wales Fire Service (Wales)	03 Heol y Nant-Whitchurch S66C-Mountain Range
B982MLS		CAV	85		Central Region Fire Brigade-**1996** Central Scotland FB(Scotland)	C1 Clackmannan Rd-Alloa S46C-F&Wylie-Scott
B411LMS		C/Unit	85		Central Region Fire Brigade-**1996** Central Scotland FB (Scotland)	F1 Linlithgow Rd-Bowness S46C-Scott
B828XHY	F/68/85	BAT	85		County of Avon Fire Brigade-**1996** Avon Fire Brigade	A1 Temple Back-Temple-Bristol S56C-Spectra
B686GSS		WRC	85		Highlands & Islands Fire Brigade (Scotland)	ex Tipper chassis & tanker body /A01 Harbour Rd-Inverness G16C-Claymore-HIFB
B317VFJ	5054	HLL	85		Devon Fire Brigade	17 Newton Rd-Torquay S75C-Angloco
C710FOD	5097	HLL FOT	85		Devon Fire Brigade	49 Crownhill Rd-Crownhill Plymouth G13C-Saxon
B880UJA C42YBA		HLL	85		Greater Manchester County Fire Service	B23 Albert Rd-Farnworth G13C-Mountain Range
C856DEU		HLL	85	92	County of Avon Fire Brigade	A2 Southmead Rd-Southmead S50C-Spectra
C857DEU	F/73/86	C/Unit	86		County of Avon Fire Brigade-**1996** Avon Fire Brigade	B7 Tenniscourt Rd-Kingswood S50C-Spectre
C745OSW		CIU Salv/T	86		Dumfries & Galloway Fire Brigade (Scotland)	D1 Brooms Rd-Dumfries **Converted Breathing Apparatus Mobile Workshops** S66C-Angloco-Penman
C503WAY		CAV	86		Leicestershire Fire Service	ND20 Epinal Way-Loughborough S66C-Leicester Carriage Builders

C710DNG		WRC	86		Norfolk Fire Service	A29 Chartwell Rd-Sprowston G16C-Angloco
D362VSA		DCU	86		Grampian Fire Brigade (Scotland)	S96 King St-Aberdeen G10C-F&Wylie
D952ETC	F/74/86	CIU	86		County of Avon Fire Brigade-**1996** Avon Fire Brigade	B4 Bonville Rd-Brislington G12C-Saxon
D999URC	CU-02	C/Unit	86		Derbyshire Fire Service	A03 Derby Rd-Ripley G13C-Customline
D415FSX		C/Unit	86		Fife Fire & Rescue Service (Scotland)	Brigade Headquarters G10C-Methven & Thomson
D937ONY		HLL	86		South Glamorgan Fire & Rescue-**1996** South Wales Fire Service (Wales)	08 Station Rd-Llantwit Major S60C-Hoskins
D93UHH	24-01	PMover	87		Cumbria Fire Service	King St-Workington G13C-Rolonoff-Ray Smith
D94UHH	24-02	PMover C/Unit	87		Cumbria Fire Service	Lorton St-Cockermouth G13C-Rolonoff-Ray Smith
D95UHH	24-03	PMover	87		Cumbria Fire Service	Warwick St-Carlisle G13C-Rolonoff-Ray Smith
D96UHH	24-04	PMover	87		Cumbria Fire Service	Abbey Rd-Barrow in Furness G13C-Rolonoff-Ray Smith
D952RBW		WRC	87		Buckinghamshire Fire & Rescue Service	East St-Olney G16C-Dairy Crest
D953RBW		CAV	87		Buckinghamshire Fire & Rescue Service	Cambridge St-Aylesbury S50C-BF&RS
D242FMS		WRC	87		Central Region Fire Brigade-**1996** Central Scotland FB (Scotland)	S6 Anderson St-Dunblane. **Re-ch Tank to Volvo FL - P482CMS** Chassis converted to SS-unit G16C-F&Wylie
D51NAF		WRC	88		Cornwall County Fire Brigade	7.1 Berrycombe Rd-Bodmin G16C-Cornwall CFB
E496UKF	1243	ET C/Unit	87		Merseyside Fire Brigade	**ex C1 Bankhall** /Reserve-Date G13C-Carmichael
E914VWL		C/Unit	87		Buckinghamshire Fire Brigade	Cambridge St-Aylesbury S50C-Carmichael
E901JYV- E930JYV E831JYV G232UUW- G249UUW	MDC-1-49	MDC	88-90		London Fire Brigade	**In 1988 London Fire Brigade started purchasing a medium sized prime mover/pod system. The locations and movements of these machines is far to extensive to note. They were designated as Medium De mountable Chassis S56C-Rawson-King & Taylor**
E555XMR		PMover FOT/ICU	88		Wiltshire Fire Brigade	3/1 Ashley Rd-Sailsbury G13TC-Multilift-Locomotors
E403DBL		CAV	88		Royal Berkshire Fire & Rescue Service	10 Denton Rd-Wokingham S50C-Locomotors
E690WSM		C/Unit	88		Dumfries & Galloway Fire Brigade (Scotland)	D1 Brooms Rd-Dumfries G08C-Scott
E818VYS		C/Unit	88		Strathclyde Fire Brigade (Scotland)	**ex C1 Kings Rd-Johnstone-1995**/Reserve- G10C-Scott
E628RRL		WRC	88		Cornwall County Fire Brigade	2.1 College St-Camborne G16C-Cornwall CFB
F431GSA		PMover	88		Grampian Fire Brigade (Scotland)	Headquarters - Converted from Waterladder Renault G13C-Multilift
F83HNS		Salv/T	89		Strathclyde Fire Brigade (Scotland)	A01 Port Dundas Rd-Cowcaddens Renault G08C-F&Wylie
F468OTN	219	WRU	89		Durham Fire & Rescue Service-**1996** Durham County Fire & Rescue Brigade	G1 Finchale Rd-Framwellgate Moor-Durham Renault S56C-Devcoplan
F326XAF		WRC	89		Cornwall County Fire Brigade	4.1 Station Rd-Truro Renault G16C-Cornwall CFB
F652BUH		FOT	89		Gwent Fire Brigade-**1996** South Wales Fire Service (Wales)	B10/47 Lighthouse Rd-Duffryn-Newport Renault G16C-Saxon

Rail Rescue Unit N842HFB is one of a pair of appliances based on the Renault G300 chassis and which operate at Avonmouth near Bristol. The Rail Rescue Concept is a system of three stages, operated in conjunction with the Great Western Railway and staffed by the Avon Fire Brigade. Stage 1 is the Alumi rail cart which carries Firefighters to the scene. The RRU is the second part and carries in pallets a multitude of rescue gear along with a rear mounted Moffat Mounty Fork Lift and operate near the Severn Tunnel. Stage 3 is a Land Rover 110 stationed at Yate, close to the Box and Chipping Sodbury tunnels.

F894ASW		PMover	89		Dumfries & Galloway Fire Brigade (Scotland)	D1 Brooms Rd-Dumfries Renault G13C-Multilift-Penman
G577YFC		WRC FOC	90		Buckinghamshire Fire & Rescue Service	Skelton Close-Beaconsfield Renault G170T-Dairy Crest
G583VNA		PMover	90		Fife Fire & Rescue Service (Scotland)	A3 Dunnikeir Rd-Kirkaldy Renault S66C-Lynton
G318MSA		PMover Heli/SU	90		Grampian Fire Brigade (Scotland)	N37 Friars Rd-Elgin Renault G13C-Multilift
H244CVR		C/Unit	90		Greater Manchester County Fire Service	A12 Bolton Rd-Agecroft Renault S56C-Harrops-GMCFS
H646VNV		PMover FOC	90		Bedfordshire Fire & Rescue Service	10 Dunstable Rd-Toddington Renault S66-Ray Smith-Palmer
J644GHY	F/65/91	OSU	91		County of Avon Fire Brigade-**1996** Avon Fire Brigade	A3 St Andrews Rd-Avonmouth Renault G300-24D-Bence/Moffat
J851WSC		C/Unit	92		Lothian & Borders Fire Brigade (Scotland)	32 Kirk Brae-Liberton-Edinburgh Renault S46-L&BFB
K479CSC		PMover Foam/C	94		Fife Fire & Rescue Service (Scotland)	A3 Dunnikier Rd-Kirkaldy Renault S66C-Lynton-FF&RS
N842HFB	F/26/95	Road Rail/U	95		Avon Fire Brigade	A03 St Andrews Rd-Avonmouth **Has under slung railway bogey for use in the nearby Severn/Box & Chipping Sodbury Railway Tunnel's .** Renault Maxter G300-24D-A G Bracey/ZweiwegMoffat
N602NHY	F23/96	Advanced Driver/T	96		Avon Fire Brigade	A01 Temple Back-Temple-Bristol Renault M230 Midliner-Saxon

Rear view of N842HFB showing rail bogeys for running on the rails.
Clive Shearman

The London Fire Brigade operated two of these ERF 84PS/Metz DLK Turntable Ladders for a number of years. Station A21 (Paddington) then a high life risk location with many major near-by fires in its history, had GYM268N, a 1974 example. It passed to Wembley for a short period in 1981. The other appliance was a 1977 example serving Lambeth, and this passed to Soho in 1981. Both were sold in 1986 though their ladders were remounted onto Volvo FL6-17 chassis. The ladders off the 1974 machine ended up on F992YCM which serves at Southport on Merseyside while the ladders off the 1977 example are now on E280NVN, at Harrogate in North Yorkshire. *The late Alan Batchelor*

ERF

Reg No	Fleet No	TYPE	YR	OS	Appliance & Brigade Name	Details/Stations
					ERF Chassied Turntable Ladders	The heavier PS chassis was chosen for mounting aerial appliances on, than the lighter PF chassis.
HOT100L		TL	72	94	Hampshire Fire Brigade	C30 North Walls Winchester 84PS-ERF Firefighter-Metz DLK30
GYM268N	TL38P	TL/P	75	86	GLC London Fire Brigade	A21 Harrow Rd-Paddington-1981 G30 Harrow Rd-Wembley-1986 **Ladders Re-ch onto Volvo FL6-17-F992YCM-Merseyside** 84PS-ERF Firefighter-Metz DLK30
PAJ576R		TL	76		North Yorkshire Fire Brigade	**ex S1 Clifford St-York-1993** /Reserve-Date 84PS-HCB Angus-Metz DLK30
OYT509R	TL39P	TL/P	77	86	GLC London Fire Brigade	B22 Albert Embankment-Lambeth- 1981 A24 Shaftsbury Ave-Soho-1983/Reserve-1986 **Ladders Re-ch onto Volvo FL6-17-Angloco E280NVN-North Yorkshire F&RS** 84PS-ERF Firefighter-Metz DLK30
UVP98S	217	TL	78		West Midlands Fire Service	**ex A1 Lancaster Circus-Central-1987** **ex D2 Dudley Rd-Brierley Hill-1993**/Reserve-Date **Originally supplied with Metz DLK30 ladders off Wolverhampton CBFB-Leyland Firemaster 9990DA** 84PS-Angloco-Magirus DL30
CNM455T		TL/P	78	89	Bedfordshire Fire Brigade	1 Barkers Lane-Bedford-1981 02 Brewers Hill Rd-Dunstable-1983 **Sold to Isle of White FB/1South St-Newport-1989** **Sold to Green King Brewery Bury St Edmonds Suffolk 1994** **Ladders Re-chassied off Bedford TKGL-769FMJ** 84PS-G&T Power-Merryweather

Reg No	Fleet No	TYPE	YR	OS	Appliance & Brigade Name	Details/Stations
		SS65 SS70 SS85 SS220 SS263 SS300			ERF Chassied Hydraulic Platforms Height 65' 70' 85' 24.0m 28.3m 32.0m	Most of the HP's were mounted on the heavier RS &PS chassis. The Pump/HP versions used the lighter PF chassis. A large number utilised the double ended crew cab by JH Jennings. The snorkels came in either 2 boom articulating heights of 65/70' ft or the 3 boom height of 85'. Later on the SS220/263/300 versions were released. They were all powered by the Perkins V8.510 engine.
EFE579E		HP	67	88	City of Lincoln Fire Brigade	South Park Ave-Lincoln-1974 A1 Lincoln-1988-Lincolnshire FB/**First in service in UK** 84RS-HCB Angus-Simon SS85
MHS9E		HP	67	85	Western Area Fire Brigade (Scotland)	Rue End St-Greenock-1975 C07 Greenock-1985 Strathclyde FB 84PS-F&Wylie-Simon SS85
NDM563E		HP	67	84	County of Flintshire Fire Brigade (Wales)	Coast Rd-Rhyl-1974 W1 Coast Rd-Rhyl-1984/County of Clwyd Fire Brigade 84PS-HCB Angus-Simon SS85
DST999E	A13	HP	67	92	Northern Area Fire Brigade (Scotland)	A1 Harbour Rd-Inverness-1975 A1 Inverness-1992 Highlands & Islands Fire Brigade 84PS-F&Wylie-Simon SS85
RXC1E	19	HP	67	88	Solihull County Borough Fire Brigade	Streetsbrook Rd-Solihull-1974 B1 Solihull-1979/Reserve-1988/West Midlands Fire Service 84RS-HCB Angus-Simon SS85

Reg	No.	Type			Fire Brigade	Details
KHY999E		PHP	67	81	City of Bristol Fire Brigade	Speedwell Rd-Speedwell-Bristol-1974 /B6 Speedwell-1981 84PFS-HCB Angus-Simon SS65
MBA773F		PHP	67	79	City of Salford Fire Brigade	Liverpool Rd-Salford-1974 A10 Salford-1977/Reserve-1979 /Greater Manchester CFS 84PFS-HCB Angus-Simon SS65
NFU121F		HP	67	91	Lindsey County Borough (Lincolnshire)	Laneham St-Scunthorpe-1974 /D1 Scunthorpe-1976 B3 Bessingby Rd-Bridlington-1976 84RS-HCB Angus-Simon SS85
KRE450F		PHP	67	88	Staffordshire Fire Brigade	ND Springfield Rd-Leek-1985 /Reserve-1988 **Sold to Tralee-Kerry Co-Irish Republic-68KY11** 84RS-HCB Angus-Simon SS65
SHN999F	195	HP	67	93	Darlington County Borough Fire Brigade	Borough Rd-Darlington-1972 St Cuthberts Way-Darlington-1974 / S1 Darlington-1993 Durham County Fire Brigade / **Sold to Bristol Lighting Co** 84PS-F&Wylie-Simon SS85
FTJ410F	452	PHP	67	77	Lancashire County Fire Brigade	E74 Bolton Rd-Agecroft-1974 A12 Agecroft-Greater Manchester CFS **Sold to Jodrell Bank- Radio Telescope** 84PS-Lancashire CFB-Simon SS65
NRY999F	HP10	HP	67	89	City of Leicester Fire Brigade	Lancaster Rd-Leicester-1974/SD 30Central-Leicestershire FS 84RS-HCB Angus-Simon SS70
PFD777F		HP	67	83	Dudley County Borough Fire Brigade	Dudley Rd-Brierley Hill-1974 D2 Brierley Hill-1977/Res-1982/West Midlands Fire Service **Booms removed and chassis used for recovery vehicle- Dennis F series cab-Bro-wreckers -CHA755Y** 84RS-HCB Angus-Simon SS65
NUE350F		HP	67	83	Warwick County Fire Brigade	SD29 Warwick St-Royal Leamington Spa-1983 **Sold to Galway County- Irish Republic-387CZM** 84RS-HCB Angus-Simon SS85
OUK999F	224	HP	67	92	Wolverhampton County Borough Fire Brigade	Merridale St-Wolverhampton-1974/E5 Wolverhampton-1980 Reserve-1992-West Midlands Fire Service 84RS-HCB Angus-Simon SS85
MVA133F		HP	67	86	Lanarkshire County Fire Brigade (Scotland)	Bothwell Rd-Hamilton-1975/E01-Hamilton-1980 E04 Main St-Coatbridge-1988- Strathclyde FB **Sold to County West Meath-Irish Republic-67WH1** 84RS-F&Wylie-Simon SS85
JDW976F		PHP	67	86	Newport County Borough FS (Wales)	Dock St-Malpas-Newport-1969/Malpas Rd-Malpas-1974 B09 Malpas-1986-Gwent Fire Brigade **Booms Re-chassied onto Dodge G16C-Saxon-D161MWO** 84RS-HCB Angus-Simon SS65
MDD747F		HP	68	83	Gloucestershire Fire Service	Keynsham Rd-Cheltenham-1974 /12 Cheltenham-1983 **Booms Re-ch onto Dodge G16C-Carmichael-A796FDG** 84RS-HCB Angus-Simon SS85
OFH999F		HP	68	83	City of Gloucester Fire Brigade	Eastern Ave-Gloucester-1974 05 Gloucester-Gloucestershire FS 84RS-HCB Angus-Simon SS85
ROA652G	57	HP	68	93	City of Birmingham Fire Brigade	10 Ettington Rd-Aston-1974 A2 Aston-1986/Reserve-1992/West Midlands Fire Service 84RS-Jennings-Simon SS85
JCL999G		PHP	68	82	City of Norwich Fire Brigade	#1 Bethel St-Norwich-1974-1984-Norfolk Fire Service **Booms Re-chassied onto Dennis F125-Dennis-XCL22X** 84PS-Jennings-Simon SS70
PMS224G		HP	68	84	Central Region Fire Brigade (Scotland)	Ranoch Rd-Stirling-1975 /S8 Stirling-1983 **Booms Re-ch onto S & Drewry WY-F&Wylie-A262JMS** 84RS-F&Wylie-Simon SS85
KFG505G		HP	68	86	Fife Fire Brigade (Scotland)	Dunnikeir Rd-Kirkaldy-1975 /A3 Kirkaldy-1986 84RS-F&Wylie-Simon SS85
JTS720G		HP	68	94	Angus Area Fire Brigade (Scotland)	Kingsway East-Dundee-1975/A11 Kingsway East-Dundee **Damaged in wall collapse at fire .Re cabbed at F&Wylie**

						Tayside Fire Brigade 84RS-F&Wylie-Simon SS85
UTX379G		HP	68	82	Glamorgan County Borough FB (Wales)	B1 Sunnyside-Bridgend-1974 01 Bridgend-1982-Mid Glamorgan FB **Booms Re-chassied onto Dodge G16C-Angloco-MTH127X** 84PS-Jennings-Simon SS85- **6 Wheeler version**
NUH800G		HP	68	86	City of Cardiff Fire Brigade (Wales)	#1 Westgate St-Cardiff-1972 #4 Heol y Nant-Whitchurch-Cardiff-1974/ 3 Whitchurch-1976 5 Port Rd-West-Barry-1986 / South Glamorgan County FB 84PS-HCB Angus-Simon SS65
JMB350G		HP	68	89	Cheshire Fire Brigade	Wellington St-Ellesmere Port-1974 /A2 Ellesmere Port-1989 84RS-Jennings-Simon SS70
TKA322G	52 **1087**	PHP	68	79	City of Liverpool Fire Brigade	12 Studholme St-Bankhall-Liverpool -1971 8 Mather Ave-Liverpool-1974 / S1Mather Ave-1979 Merseyside Fire Brigade 84PFS-HCB Angus-Simon SS50
SVK987G	125	HP	68	84	Newcastle & Gateshead Joint Fire Service	A2 Fossway-Walker-Newcastle-1974 /F Fossway-Walker-1975 J Preston North Rd-Tynmouth-1984 / Tyne & Wear MFB 84RS-F&Wylie-Simon SS85
WWE980G		HP	68	85	City of Sheffield Fire Brigade	Division St-Sheffield-1974 / C1 Division St-Sheffield-1985 South Yorkshire County FS 84PS-HCB Angus-Simon SS85
SNW961G		HP	69	89	Leeds City Fire Brigade	Kirkstall Rd-Leeds-1974 /D11 Kirkstall Rd-Leeds-1989 West Yorkshire Fire Service 84PS-HCB Angus-Simon SS85
UFD342G		PHP	71	?	Kent Fire Brigade	**ex Demonstrator** / 89 Margate Rd-Thanet-? 35 Coldharbour Rd-Thameside-? 84PFS-HCB Angus-Simon SS50
NFC684H		HP	70	92	City of Oxford Fire Brigade	Rewley Rd-Oxford-1974 /B1 Rewley Rd-Oxfordshire FS-1992 **Damaged in an RTA** 84PS-HCB Angus-Simon SS70

Hydraulic Platform NFU121F is based on the ERF 84RS chassis and carried Simon SS85 booms in its role with the Lindsey County Fire Brigade until 1974. It was delivered from HCB Angus in 1967 to Laneham Street fire station in Scunthorpe. In 1974 it passed to the then newly formed Humberside Brigade to serve until 1991, ending up at Bridlington before withdrawal. The Humberside Fire Brigade inherited two ERF HPs in 1974, the other coming from the City of Kingston up on Hull FB In the form of a Pump Hydraulic Platform with Simon SS50 booms.
Norman Downs

FPO135H		HP	70	77	West Sussex Fire Brigade	A01 Ardsheal Rd-Worthing- **?** A20 West Meads Drive-Bognor Regis-**Written off in RTA** 84RS-Jennings-Simon SS85-**Yellow Booms**
XDN494J	No-1	PHP	70	80	City of York Fire Brigade	Clifford St-York-1974 / S1 York-1980-North Yorkshire FB **Sold to Carlow County Irish Republic-TIC224** 84PFS-HCB Angus-Simon SS50-**Yellow livery**
RBF778J		HP	70	94	Staffordshire Fire Brigade	Lammascote Rd-Stafford-1988 / Reserve-1994 **Sold to Irish Republic** 84PS-Jennings-Simon SS70
LBP773J		HP	71	79	West Sussex Fire Brigade	A17 Northgate-Chichester 84RS-HCB Angus-Simon SS85-**Yellow Booms**
MPX842J		HP	71	89	West Sussex Fire Brigade	A12 Hurst Rd-Horsham-1981 /A01 Ardsheal Rd-Worthing 84RS HCB Angus-Simon SS85-**Yellow Booms**
YKH681J		PHP	71	83	City of Kingston upon Hull Fire Brigade	#1Worship St-Hull-1974 /A1 Worship St-Hull Central-1983 Training Centre-Humberside FB 84PFS-Jennings-Simon SS50
SWH222J		HP	71	83	Bolton County Borough Fire Brigade	#1 Moor Lane-Bolton-1974 B20 Moor Lane-Bolton-1983 /Greater Manchester CFS 84PS-HCB Angus-Simon SS85
CYC515J		PHP	71	90	Somerset Fire Brigade	21 Reckleford-Yeovil 84PFS-HCB Angus-Simon SS50
BTD719J	75	PHP	71	83	Lancashire County Fire Brigade	11.2 Liverpool Rd-Eccles-1974 A13 Eccles-1983/Greater Manchester CFS 84PS-HCB Angus-Simon SS85
YBU999J		PHP	71	83	Oldham County Borough Fire Brigade	Ascroft St-Oldham-1974 C33 Oldham-1983 /Greater Manchester CFS 84RS-Jennings-Simon SS70
VHL526J		HP	71	88	Wakefield County Borough Fire Brigade	Brunswick St-Wakefield-1974 F11 Wakefield-1988 /West Yorkshire Fire Service 84RS-Jennings-Simon SS70
LFT443J	141	PHP	71	84	Tynemouth County Borough Fire Brigade	Preston North Rd-1974 /J Tynemouth-1984 **Re-built after severe RTA Damage** 84PFS-HCB Angus-Simon SS50
OPT551J	192	HP	71	93	Durham County Fire Brigade	A1 Framwellgate Moor-Durham-1993 84RS-Jennings-Simon SS85
TXJ647K		HP	71	83	City of Manchester Fire Brigade	Moss Lane East-Moss-side-Manchester-1972 Denhill Rd-Moss-side-1974 D44 Mosside-1983/Greater Manchester CFS 84RS-HCB Angus-Simon SS85
VDB953K		PHP	71	84	Stockport County Borough Fire Brigade	#1 Whitehill St-Stockport-1974 D40 Whitehill St-Stockport-1976 A10 Liverpool Rd-Salford-1984 /Greater Manchester CFS 84PFS-Jennings-Simon SS50
FNG779K		HP	71		Norfolk Fire Service	B47 Kilhams Way-Kings Lynn 84PS-HCB Angus-Simon SS70
FTN67K	106	PHP	72	84	Newcastle & Gateshead Joint Fire Service	A3 West Rd-West End-Newcastle-1974 B West End-1984/Tyne & Wear Metropolitan FB 84PFS-HCB Angus-Simon SS50
FVK544K	110	PHP	72	82	Newcastle & Gateshead Joint Fire Service	A1 Pilgrim St-Newcastle Central-1974 D Newcastle Central-1982 **Written off after Severe fire in workshops-Gateshead** 84PFS-HCB Angus-Simon SS50
SRB356K		HP	72	91	Derbyshire Fire Service	B1 Compton Grove-Buxton 84RS-HCB Angus-Simon SS70
PCK999K	262	HP	72	96	Preston County Borough Fire Brigade	Blackpool Rd-Preston-1974 C50 Blackpool Rd-Preston-1980 Lancashire County FB 02 Salmon Parade-Bridgewater-Date Somerset Fire Brigade 84PS-HCB Angus-Simon SS70

DNJ12K		HP	72	93	East Sussex Fire Brigade	B22 Beeching Rd-Bexhill 84RS-HCB Angus-Simon SS85
FBH868K		HP	72	88	Buckinghamshire Fire Brigade	C1 St Marys St-High Wycombe **Booms Re-chassied onto Dodge G16C-Saxon-E379DBL** 84PS-HCB Angus-Simon SS70
GNX999K		HP	72	87	Warwick County Fire Brigade	ND 20 Newtown Rd-Nuneaton-1987 84RS-HCB Angus-Simon SS70
XDL62K		HP	72	95	Isle of Wight Fire Brigade	1 South St-Newport-Date 84RS-HCB Angus-Simon SS85
FCG70K		HP	72	89	Hampshire Fire Brigade	A1 West Ham Close-Basingstoke **Booms Re-chassied onto Dodge G16C-Saxon-F994NRV** 84PS-HCB Angus-Simon SS70
GOR70K		HP	72	88	Hampshire Fire Brigade	B17 West St-Fareham **Booms Re-chassied onto Dodge G16C-Saxon-E741HRV** 84PS-HCB Angus-Simon SS70
BCR822K		HP	72	87	City of Southampton Fire Brigade	St Mary's Rd-St Marys-Southampton-1974 D54 St Marys-Southampton-1987 **Booms Re-chassied onto Dodge G16C-Saxon-D623DTR** 84PS-HCB Angus-Simon SS70
SVE668K		PHP	72	83	Cambridgeshire Fire & Rescue Service	Parkside-Cambridge-1974 B1Parkside-Cambridge-1983 84PFS-HCB Angus-Simon SS50
KRR999K		HP	72	92	City of Mansfield Fire Brigade	Rosemary St-Mansfield-1974 A01 Mansfield-1992-Nottinghamshire Fire Brigade 84PS-HCB Angus-Simon SS70
KDM860K		HP	72	93	County of Flintshire Fire Brigade (Wales)	Chester Rd-Deeside-1974 /E2 Deeside-1986 W1 Coast Rd-Rhyl-1993-Clwyd CFS 84RS-Jennings-Simon SS85
UEN999L		PHP	72	82	Bury County Borough Fire Brigade	The Rock-Bury-1974 C36 The Rock-Bury-1982/Greater Manchester CFS 84PFS-Jennings-Simon SS50
VJL11L		HP	72	94	Holland County Borough (Lincolnshire)	Robin Hoods Walk-Boston-1974 C1 Boston-1989-Lincolnshire FB B1 Churchill Ave-Skegness-1994 84RS-HCB Angus-Simon SS70
SXD411L		HP	72	91	Luton County Borough Fire Brigade	Studley Rd-Luton-1974 0 Studley Rd-Luton-Bedfordshire FB **Sold to Clare County-Shannon-Irish Republic-1991** 84RS-HCB Angus-Simon SS85
EKB42L	1121	PHP	72	80	City of Liverpool Fire Brigade	12 West Derby Rd-Liverpool-1974 N5 West Derby Rd-1980 /Merseyside Fire Brigade 84PFS-ERF-Simon SS50
XFR538L	242	HP	72	90	Blackpool County Borough Fire Brigade	South Shore-Blackpool-1974 / A30 Albert Rd-1980 C50 Blackpool Rd-1990 -Lancashire County Fire Brigade 84RS-HCB Angus-Simon SS70
FHE999L		HP	72		Barnsley County Borough Fire Brigade	**ex Broadway-Barnsley-1974 /A1 Broadway-Barnsley-1989** Reserve/Training-Date-South Yorkshire County FS 84PF-Jennings-Simon SS85
TCH182L		HP	73	91	Derby County Borough Fire Brigade	D3 Kingsway-Derby-1974 /D1 Ascot Drive-Derby-1988 Derbyshire Fire Service/Reserve-1991 84PS-Jennings-Simon SS85
LJH71L		HP	73	86	Hertfordshire County Council Fire Brigade	A09 Whippendell Rd-Watford **Cab destroyed in a wall collapse and repaired at Angloco's** 84PS-HCB Angus-Simon SS70
LJH73L		HP	73	89	Hertfordshire County Council Fire Brigade	B11 Harpenden Rd-St Albans 84PS-HCB Angus-Simon SS85

The old & the new ERF A Series Bulk Foam Carrier NKF470F looks typical of the large Petrol and Bulk Tankers of the time. Previously a Brewery Lorry it was bought in the early 1970s by the Cheshire County FB for use at Ellesmere Port. The area was rapidly developing into the major petro/chemical centre, so the need for large quantities of foam were becoming apparent. This machine served until it was replaced by a Dennis Delta II in 1978. *Michael Lawmon*

Newly delivered to the Greater Manchester CFS, ERF Foam Tanker P330FVR is one of four with a capacity of 9,000 litres and one of the appliances to replace the Ford D Series units at Cheadle and Philips Park, a Dodge G Series at Sale and a Leyland Roadrunner at Farnworth. The tank is supplied by Clayton Tankers and the bodywork is by Saxon of Sanbec. This series of chassis will take the ERF company into the next millenium.
Gavin Stewart

In 1973 the London Fire Brigade took delivery of a Hydraulic Platforms, having previously only operated Turntable Ladders. Two examples were delivered of which TLO101M, seen here, was of type ERF 84PS with HCB Angus bodywork. The other appliance was TLO102M, a Dennis F123 Series. Both machines were fitted with Simon SS70 booms. Later, the Dennis unit was returned and no further ERF chassis were ordered though the London Fire Brigade acquired fifteen SS220 HPs in the 1980s based on Dennis F125, Dodge G16 and Shelvoke & Drewry WY chassis with many examples having their booms later rechassied onto the Volvo FL6-18 chassis. *The late Alan Batchelor*

OYB999L		PHP	73	90	Somerset Fire Brigade	01 Lisieux Way-Taunton 84PFS-ERF-Simon SS50
ABO665L		HP	73	93	City of Cardiff Fire Brigade (Wales)	#1 Adam St-Cardiff-1974 1 Adam St-Cardiff-1993 /South Glamorgan County FB 84RS-HCB Angus-Simon SS85
NWD999M		HP	73	90	Warwick County Fire Brigade	ND 26 Corporation St-Rugby 84RS-HCB Angus-Simon SS70
ORV713M		HP	73	95	City of Portsmouth Fire Brigade	#3 Wayte St-Cosham-Portsmouth-1974/B23 Cosham-1978/B24 Somers Rd-Southsea-Portsmouth-Date-Hampshire FB **Sold to Dungarven-Waterford County FS-Irish Republic** 84PS-HCB Angus-Simon SS70-**Originally SS220**
TLO101M	HP1P	PHP	73	90	GLC London Fire Brigade	L25 Rainham Rd-Dagenham-1986/N/Reserve-1990) **Sold to Office Cleaning Services Ltd-North Yorkshire** 84PS-HCB Angus-Simon SS70
OUN543M		HP	74	95	County of Clwyd Fire Service (Wales)	W2 Abergale Rd-Colwyn Bay-1986 2 Chester Rd-Deeside-Date 84RS-Jennings-Simon SS70
GVR893N		HP	74	86	Greater Manchester County Fire Service	E50 London Rd-Manchester-1986 84PS-HCB Angus-Simon SS220
NMN999		HP	75	92	Isle of Man Fire Brigade	1 Peel Rd-Douglas **Booms Re-ch onto Volvo FL6-17-Carmichael-NMN999** 84PS-HCB Angus-Simon SS220
KVP178P	135	HP	76		West Midlands Fire Service	**ex B3 Radford Rd-Coventry-1990/ Reserve-Date** **C7 Icknield Port Rd-Ladywood—Stand in for J43SOF** **Cancelled export order to the Middle East** 84PS-ERF-Simon SS85
KVP179P	295	HP	76	95	West Midlands Fire Service	E1 Blue Lane West-Walsall-1986 A6 Washwood Heath Rd-Ward End-1992/Reserve-Date **Cancelled export order to the Middle East** 84PS-ERF-Simon SS85
NMA397P		PHP	76	86	Cheshire Fire Brigade	Macon Way-Crewe-1974 /C1 Macon Way-Crewe-1982 B1 Winwick St-Warrington-1986 84PFS-ERF-Simon SS50
SCD885R		HP	77		East Sussex Fire Brigade	A02 English Close-Hove 84CS-ERF-Simon SS263
PBA861R		HP	77	90	Greater Manchester County Fire Service	B21 Crompton Way-Bolton-1988/Reserve-1990 84CS-ERF-Simon SS220
PBA862R		HP	77	92	Greater Manchester County Fire Service	E54 Hodgeson St-Ashton u Lyne-1983 D44 Denhill Rd-Moss-side-1989/Reserve-1990 84CS-ERF-Simon SS263
POB982R	300	HP	77	96	West Midlands Fire Service	C7 Icknield Port Rd-Ladywood-1992 Reserve-1995 Booms **Re-chassied onto ERF ES8-P266EON** 84CS-ERF-Simon SS263
DOJ114V	108	HP	80	92	West Midlands Fire Service	B1 Streetsbrook Rd-Solihull- **Written off after collapsing at a fete in which a number of people were injured** 84PS-Angloco-Simon SS263-**Perkins V8-640**
						ERF returned with a new range of chassis to the Fire Engine market in the late 1980's. It was not until the mid 1990's that a suitable heavy chassis was available to mount a Hydraulic Platform onto.
P266EON	112	ALP	96		West Midlands Fire Service	B1 Streetsbrook Road-Solihull **Booms Re-ch off ERF84CS-POB982R ex C7 Ladywood** EC8-Saxon-Simon SS263
P267EON	125	ALP	96		West Midlands Fire Service	EC8-Saxon-Simon SS263
P268EON	118	ALP	96		West Midlands Fire Service	EC8-Saxon-Simon SS263
P		PHP	97		Wiltshire Fire Brigade	4.1 Hilperton Rd-Trowbridge EC10-GB Fire-Italmec NCS

					ERF Chassied Specialist Appliances	Most ERF specialist appliances were mounted on the lighter PF chassis. This chassis was also used for the Pumping Appliance market.
NKF470F		Foam/C	67	78	Cheshire County Fire Brigade	**ex Brewery Lorry** / Wellington Rd-Ellesmere Port-1974 A2 Wellington Rd-Ellesmere Port-1978 A Series-CCFB
OBF198J		Rec/V	70		Staffordshire Fire Brigade	**ex WRT Kidsgrove-1986/**Brigade Workshops 84PF-HCB Angus/SFB
UFV400K	247	Pump/ET	71	82	Blackpool County Borough Fire Brigade	B30 Albert Rd-Blackpool-1974 A30-Albert Rd-Blackpool-Lancashire County FB 84PF-HCB Angus
TDK999K		ET	72	81	Rochdale County Borough Fire Brigade	Maclure Rd-Rochdale-1974 C30 Maclure Rd-Rochdale-1981 Greater Manchester CFS 84PF-HCB Angus
NMA218L		WRC	72	91	East Sussex Fire Brigade	13 Beacon Drive-Crowborough 84PF-ESFB
VGR265L		ET/CU	72	91	City of Sunderland	#1 Dun Cow St-Sunderland-1974 N Dun Cow St-Sunderland-1988 T Victoria St West-Hebburn-1989 K Kepple St-South Shields-1991/Tyne & Wear M FB 84PF-HCB Angus
RTH431S		ET/CU	78	91	West Glamorgan County Fire Service (Wales)	1 Cimla Rd-Neath **/Preserved** 84PF-ERF Firefighter
E784JEH	548	C/Unit	87		Staffordshire Fire & Rescue Service	**ex ND Uttoxeter Rd-Longton-1995** ND Springfield Rd-Leek E6.18 Hi-line-John Dennis CB
F616EWJ		C/Unit	89		South Yorkshire County Fire Service	ED 8 Highwoods Rd-Mexborough E6.18 Hi-line-Angloco
K335BHB		WRC	93		Mid Glamorgan Fire Service-**1996** South Wales Fire Service (Wales)	15 Oxford St Trefforest Pontypridd ES8-Dairy Products Engineering
M101KBO		WRC	95		Mid Glamorgan Fire Service-**1996** South Wales Fire Service (Wales)	01 Angel St-Sunnyside-Bridgend ES8-Massey Tankers
N170KAM		PMover	95		Wiltshire Fire Brigade	1/4 Highworth Rd-Stratton-**Chemical & Environmental PU** ES8-Multilift
P		FOT	96		Cheshire Fire Brigade	
P		FOT	96		Cheshire Fire Brigade	
P264EON	301	PMover	96		West Midlands Fire Service	A5 College Rd-Perry Bar EC8-Multilift
P265EON	302	PMover	96		West Midlands Fire Service	EC8-Multilift
N635XBA		FOT	96		Greater Manchester County Fire Service	E52 Briscoe Lane-Phillips Park EC8-Saxon-Clayton Tankers
P330FVR		FOT	96		Greater Manchester County Fire Service	D47 Turves Rd-Cheadle Hulme EC8-Saxon-Clayton Tankers
P331FVR		FOT	97		Greater Manchester County Fire Service	
P332FVR		FOT	97		Greater Manchester County Fire Service	
P337GBA		SI/Unit	97		Greater Manchester County Fire Service	B23 Albert Rd-Farnworth EC8-Don Bur-**Moffat Mounty**

KARRIER

Reg No	Fleet No	TYPE	YR	OS	Appliance & Brigade Name	Details/Stations
						The Gamecock chassis superseded the very popular Bantam which was a 2 Ton pre war chassis. It had an similar cab to the Commer QX.
LAP7		FOT	54	75	East Sussex County Fire Brigade	Hove St-Hove /English Close-Hove-1974 A2 English Close Hove-1975/East Sussex County FB Gamecock-Carmichael
KPN97		Pump SalvT	54	72	East Sussex County Fire Brigade	Hamherst Rd-Bexhill-1974 Gamecock-Carmichael
KJR135		ET	56	79	Northumberland County Fire Brigade	**ex Hose Reel Tender-Bellingham-1970/** Newburn-1979 Gamecock 72A-Miles
KJR136		ET	56	80	Northumberland County Fire Brigade	**ex Hose Reel Tender-Rothbury-1970/** Blyth-1980 Gamecock 72A-Miles
LJR394		ET	57	80	Northumberland County Fire Brigade	**ex Hose Reel Tender-Berwick-1970/** Berwick-1980 Gamecock 72A-Miles
LJR395		ET	57	80	Northumberland County Fire Brigade	**ex Hose Reel Tender- Alnwick-1969/** Alnwick-1980 Gamecock 72A-Miles
RWO698		ET	57	73	Monmouthshire Fire Brigade (Wales)	17 New Rd-New Inn-Pontypool Gamecock 72A-Buttons
MNL785		ET	58	76	Northumberland County Fire Brigade	**ex Hose Reel Tender-Morpeth-1969/** Morpeth-1976 **Converted to Decontamination Unit-1982** Gamecock 72A-Miles
MNL786		ET	58	81	Northumberland County Fire Brigade	**ex Hose Reel Tender-Hexham-1970/** Hexham-1981 **Converted to Tow Truck after being sold OOS** Gamecock 72A-Miles
20LMX	ST-5	Salv/T	58	72	Middlesex Fire Brigade	69 Faggs Rd-Feltham-1965 D28 Faggs Rd-Feltham-1972-London Fire Brigade Gamecock-Middlesex FB
RWO999		Foam/T	58	?	Monmouthshire Fire Brigade (Wales)	**ex WRT** Gamecock-Buttons-MFB
26WMX	ST-6	Salv/T	59	72	Middlesex Fire Brigade	38 Waxlow Rd-Park Royal(Harlesdon) 1965 G29 Waxlow Rd-Park Royal-1972-London Fire Brigade Gamecock-Middlesex FB
9338MM	ST-7	Salv/T	61	72	Middlesex Fire Brigade	2 High St-Southgate-1965 J28 High St Southgate-1972-London Fire Brigade Gamecock-Middlesex FB
TPM133		BAT	61	78	East Sussex County Fire Brigade	Hove St-Hove/English Close-Hove-1974 A2 English Close-Hove-1975/East Sussex County FB **Converted FoT**-A6 Fort Rd-Newhaven-1979 Gamecock-Carmichael
PYJ206		FOT	63	76	Angus Area Fire Brigade (Scotland)	**ex WRT**-Central-Dundee-1970 Ponderlaw St-Arbroath-1975 A3 Arbroath-1976-Tayside FB - Converted into WRT Gamecock-Carmichael
HAE999D		Foam/C	66	79	City of Bristol Fire Brigade	#3 St Andrews Rd-Avonmouth-1974 A3 Avonmouth-1979-County of Avon Fire Brigade VAC-HCB Angus

Karrier Gamecock Hose Reel Tender KJR135 had already given 14 years service when, in 1970, it was converted into an Emergency Tender. Six were converted with this example based at Newburn, Northumberland. Others were loacted at Blyth, Berwick, Alnwick, Morpeth and Hexham and saw service into the 1980s. This photograph shows the restrictive enterance to the crew cab and that the starting handle remained in place. *Ian Moore*

MISCELLANEOUS APPLIANCES

Reg No	Fleet No	TYPE	YR	OS	Appliance & Brigade Name	Details/Stations
HT3528		Ladder	20	35 ?	City of Bristol	Bridewell St-Bristol-**Collapsed at Fire** Aster-Merryweather-85 L Wooden
SG4075		TL	21	42 ?	Edinburgh Fire Brigade	? Aster-Merryweather-85 L Wooden
?		TL	23	42 ?	Bournemouth Fire Brigade	Holdenhurst Rd-Bournemouth Aster-Merryweather-85 L Wooden
?		Ladder	06	21	City of Bristol	Bridewell St-Bristol Belsize-Morris-Magirus-66 L Wooden-**ex Horse Drawn**
?		Ladder	12	?	City of Leicester	? Belsize-Morris-Magirus-85 L Wooden
OI1954		Ladder	12	42 ?	Londonderry Fire Brigade	Londonderry Belsize-Magirus 85' Wooden
JHT854	CU-3	C/Unit	47	67	LCC London Fire Brigade	Stratford 59-67 Bristol L5G-LFB
XB9610		Electric Ladder	02		LCC London Fire Brigade	? **Re-ch Tilling Stevens-1920** Cedes Electric-Morris-Magirus-85 L Wooden-**ex H Drawn**
		Electric Ladder	08		LCC London Fire Brigade	? **Re-ch Tilling Stevens-1921** Cedes Electric-Morris-Magirus-85 L Wooden-**ex H Drawn**
		Electric Ladder	08		LCC London Fire Brigade	? **Re-ch Tilling Stevens -1921** Cedes Electric-Morris-Magirus-85 L Wooden-**ex H Drawn**
		Electric Ladder	09		LCC London Fire Brigade	? **Re-ch Tilling Stevens-1922** Cedes Electric-Morris-Magirus-85 L Wooden-**ex H Drawn**
LC7349		Electric Ladder	09		LCC London Fire Brigade	? **Re-ch Tilling Stevens-1922** Cedes Electric-Morris-Magirus-85 L Wooden-**ex H Drawn**
LC5027		Electric Ladder	12		LCC London Fire Brigade	? Cedes Electric-Morris-Magirus 85 L Wooden
LH8800		Electric Ladder	13		LCC London Fire Brigade	? Cedes Electric-Morris-Magirus 85 L Wooden
LH8801		Electric Ladder	13		LCC London Fire Brigade	? Cedes Electric-Morris-Magirus 85 L Wooden
YAO457Y		Rec/V	82		Mid Glamorgan Fire Service-**1996** South Wales Fire Service (Wales)	Brigade Workshops Daf 3300 Interstater Wreckers International
JNY537D		Rec/V	66		Mid Glamorgan Fire Service-**1996** South Wales Fire Service (Wales)	Brigade Workshops Diamond T-Holmes-MGFS
H192MRW		BASU	91		Royal Berkshire Fire & Rescue Service	A03 Dee Rd-Reading Ducato Maxi-RBF&RS
H193MRW		BASU	91		Royal Berkshire Fire & Rescue Service	C19 Bridge Rd-Maidenhead Ducato Maxi-RBF&RS
KYS916V		TSU	80		Strathclyde Fire Brigade (Scotland)	**E1 Bothwell Rd-Hamilton-1988** Fiat F10-F&Wylie
RUS225W		C/Unit	80	88	Strathclyde Fire Brigade (Scotland)	**E1 Bothwell Rd-Hamilton** Fiat F10-F&Wylie
						The GMC (General Motors Corporation) Chevrolet K -3500 chassis has proved very versatile in its uses from Rapid Intervention Vehicles to Rescue Tenders.
C206TDP		RSV	86		Royal Berkshire Fire & Rescue Service	**ex 04 Hawthorne Rd-Newbury-1992**/Reserve K30-Locomotors
B216NVT		Res/T	85	86	Cambridgeshire Fire & Rescue Service	B01 Parkside-Cambridge -1986-**Written off in RTA** K30-Woodway

C630LFL		Res/T	86		Cambridgeshire Fire & Rescue Service	**B01 Parkside-Cambridge-1994-**Reserve -Date **Body from -K30-B216NVT-**Front mounted winch K30-Woodway
D640EEW		Res/T	87	89	Cambridgeshire Fire & Rescue Service	A14 Dogsthorpe Rd-Peterborough **Destroyed in Explosion-Fireman Killed** K30-Woodway-**Van shape**
D277BFH	665	Res/T	87	96	Gloucestershire Fire & Rescue Service	Reserve- 1996/**Stored at 12 Keynshem Rd-Cheltenham-** K30-Carmichael-GF&RS
E933YBH		Res/U	87		Bedfordshire Fire & Rescue Service	12 Southfields Rd-Kempston K30-HCB Angus
E934YBH		Res/U	87		Bedfordshire Fire & Rescue Service	13 Stopsley Way-Stopsley-Luton K30-HCB Angus
E124FCJ		ET	88	97	Hereford & Worcester Fire Brigade	25 Windsor St-Bromsgrove/Front mounted winch K30-HCB Angus
E125FCJ		ET	88	91	Hereford & Worcester Fire Brigade	46 Owen St-Hereford/**Written off in RTA-Body remounted** K30-HCB Angus
F151BAT		Res/T	88		Humberside Fire Brigade	**ex A3 Hull North-1993/**Reserve- Front mounted winch K30-HCB Angus
F349FWL		MSU	88		Buckinghamshire Fire & Rescue Service	5.1 St Marys St-High Wycombe-1992 **Converted Breathing Appt/T-**High St-Waddesdon- K30-Mountain Range-BF&RS
F761FAW	75	Res/T Water/RU	88		Shropshire Fire & Rescue Service	**ex RIV-1991-Withdrawn due to RTA** St Michael's St-Shrewsbury-Tow's a inshore rescue boat K30-Telehoist
F291OGM		RSV	89		Royal Berkshire Fire & Rescue Service	17 Tuns Lane-Slough K30-Excalibur
F261VAD	701	Res/T	89		Gloucestershire Fire & Rescue Service	07 Pagen Hill-Stroud-Front mounted winch K30-Tele-Hoist
F368KTU		OSU	89		Cheshire Fire Brigade	**ex C1 Crewe Rescue/T-1993** C9 West St-Congleton-Winch fitted K30-Macclesfield MB
F369KTU		OSU	89		Cheshire Fire Brigade	**ex A1 Chester Rescue/T-1993** A2 Wellington Rd-Ellesmere Port -Winch fitted K30-Macclesfield MB
F156SRE		Res/T	89		Tyne & Wear Fire Brigade	EDN Railway Row-Sunderland -Winch fitted K30-Locomotors
F157SRE		Res/T	89		Tyne & Wear Fire Brigade	NDF Fossway Walker-Newcastle-Winch fitted K30-Locomotors
G830PNX		Res/T	89		Tyne & Wear Fire Brigade	SDT Victoria Rd-Hebburn-Winch fitted K30-Reynolds Boughton
G117TAP		OSU	90		East Sussex Fire Brigade	04 Preston Circus-Brighton K30-Macclesfield MB
G118TAP		OSU	90		East Sussex Fire Brigade	**ex 12 Keld Avenue-Uckfield-1993** 11 Whitley Rd-Eastbourne K30-Macclesfield MB
G119TAP		OSU	90		East Sussex Fire Brigade	**ex 18 London Rd-Battle-1993** 08 Bohemia Rd-Hastings K30-Macclesfield MB
G781FWP		ET	90		Hereford & Worcester Fire Brigade	21 Copenhagen St-Worcester-Front mounted winch K30-HCB Angus
H913TUY		ET	91		Hereford & Worcester Fire Brigade	46 Owen St-Hereford/**Body off E125FCJ-**FM winch K30-HCB Angus
H962GPA		RIV	90		Surrey Fire & Rescue Service	14 Eastbourne Rd-Godstone-Front mounted winch K30-Boughton
H963GPA		RIV	90		Surrey Fire & Rescue Service	33 Addelstone Moor-Chertsey-Front mounted winch K30-Boughton
H442AMA		OSU	91		Cheshire Fire Brigade	**ex B1 Warrington Rescue/T-1993** B1 Winwick Rd-Warrington-Front mounted winch K30-Jennings

H443AMA		OSU	91		Cheshire Fire Brigade	**ex B3 Knutsford Rescue/T-1993** C1 Macon Way-Crewe-Front mounted winch K30-Jennings
K402EET		RRU	92		South Yorkshire County Fire Service	E19 Oaks Lane-Rotherham-Winch fitted K31403-Angloco
K386FET		RRU	92		South Yorkshire County Fire Service	E28 Edlington Lane-Edlington-Winch fitted K31403-Angloco
K838JWB		RRU	93		South Yorkshire County Fire Service	W25 Mansfield Rd-Sheffield-Winch fitted K31403-Saxon
K839JWB		RRU	93		South Yorkshire County Fire Service	**ex E9 Union Rd-Thorne-1995**/ 26 Tankersley- K31403-Saxon Winch fitted
K219XPF		RIV	93		Surrey Fire & Rescue Service	21 Gavell Rd-Painshill -Front mounted winch K30-Boughton
325EYR		WRC	61	78	Bedfordshire Fire Service	Kempston Fire Station-1971 Southfields Rd-Kempston-1978 Guy Warrior-Sun Engineering
CAC571B		ET	52	77	Warwick County Fire Brigade	**ex Army-1964** A5 Corporation St-Rugby-1977 Humber 4x4-WCFB
CMJ392D	120	Light4R	66	73	Bedfordshire Fire Service	2 Brewers Hill Rd-Dunstable Humber 4x4-College of Aeronautics
CMJ393D	121	Light4R	66	73	Bedfordshire Fire Service	5 Chesnut Ave-Biggleswade-1973 Humber 4x4-College of Aeronautics
CMJ394D	122	Light4R	66	73	Bedfordshire Fire Service	1 Barkers Lane-Bedford Humber 4x4-College of Aeronautics
CMJ395D	123	Utility Van	66	73	Bedfordshire Fire Service	2 Brewers Hill-Dunstable Humber 4x4-College of Aeronautics
DBM151D	124	Light4R	66	73	Bedfordshire Fire Service	10 Dunstable Rd-Toddington Humber 4x4-College of Aeronautics
JDE60E		ET/Spec Eqp/T	66	76	Pembrokeshire Fire Brigade (Wales)	Merlins Wall-Haverfordwest-1974-Dyfed FB Humber 4x4-PFB
						The Jeep 320/40 chassis has been used only occasionally by Brigades in the UK. It was powered by a 3.0 litre American Motors engine.
GWV999V		Res/T	80	90	East Sussex Fire Brigade	A04 Preston Circus-Brighton J20-Pilcher-Greene
A778EPN		Res/T	84	95	East Sussex Fire Brigade	**ex B12 Keld Ave-Uckfield-1990** B22 Beeching Rd-Bexhill- J20-Angloco
A779EPN		Res/T	84		East Sussex Fire Brigade	**ex B18 London Rd-Battle-1990** A01 North St-Lewes- J20-Angloco
B527URO	512	Res/T	84	96	Staffordshire Fire Brigade	**ex Springfield Rd-Leek-1988** **ex Giggetty Lane-Wombourne-1995** /Reserve- J20-Fulton & Wylie
B528URO	508	Res/T	84	96	Staffordshire Fire Brigade	Birmingham Rd-Lichfield J20-Fulton & Wylie
B331OJK		Res/T	85	90	East Sussex Fire Brigade	B08 Bohemia Rd-Hastings J20-Angloco
E935JFA	547	Res/T	88		Staffordshire Fire Brigade	**ex Springfield Rd-Leek-1995** /Birmingham Rd-Lichfield- J20-John Dennis CB
L411SHT	A/01/93	HLL	93		County of Avon Fire Brigade-**1996** Avon Fire Brigade	**A2 Southmead Rd-Southmead** **Mitsubishi L200 Pick-up-AFB**
L412SHT	A/08/93	River/RU	93		County of Avon Fire Brigade-**1996** Avon Fire Brigade	**B1 Cleveland Bridge-Bath** **Mitsubishi L200 Pick-up-AFB**
L413SHT	A//10/93	Cliff/RU	93		County of Avon Fire Brigade-**1996** Avon Fire Brigade	**C1 Milton Ave-Weston Super Mare** **Mitsubishi L200 Pick-up-AFB**
F666AEX		Water Res/U	89		Norfolk Fire Service	**ex A27 Norwich-1993** **Converted Salvage Tender**/ A23 Whitegates-Hethersett Renault Traffic T35-NFS

'Commer Cob' Breathing Apparatus Control Vehicle JYW34D was photographed at B21 Clapham in 1971. The London Fire Brigade operated seven in od rge Cobs in this role at Divisional stations. *The late Alan Batchelor*

This picture of WXP127, a 1959 Hillman Husky, was a Breathing Apparatus Control Vehicle with the London Fire Brigade. It was taken at station B29 (New Cross) in 1966. They operated five in this role. *The late Alan Batchelor*

K643DEW		BAT C/Unit	93		Norfolk Fire Service	Headquarters Renault Traffic T35-West's-NFS	
L279VSW		ISU	94		Dumfries & Galloway Fire Brigade (Scotland)	D1 Brooms Rd-Dumfries Renault Messenger B110-D&GFB	
L281VSW		ISU	94		Dumfries & Galloway Fire Brigade (Scotland)	B6 Arthur St-Newton Stewart Renault Messenger B110-D&GFB	
M732CBX		BAT S/Unit	95		East Sussex County Fire Brigade	20Frerry Rd-Rye Renault Traffic T35-Bott	
M733CBX		BAT S/Unit	95		East Sussex County Fire Brigade	05 Roedean Rd-Roedean-Brighton Renault Traffic T35-Bott	
F920NHK		HRV	89		Essex County Fire & Rescue Service	B34 Rainsford Lane-Chelmsford **Fitted HIAB 071 crane** Scammell S24-Wreckers International	
?		Ladder	06	?	Glasgow Fire Service	? Simonis-Mercedes-Braun-85 L Wooden	
?		Ladder	07	21	City of Liverpool	#1 Hatton Gardens-Liverpool Simonis-Magirus 85'L	
?		Ladder	?	23	City of Sheffield	? Simonis-Braun-84 L Wooden	
?		Ladder	10	21?	Edinburgh Fire Brigade	Lauriston Place-Edinburgh Simonis-Braun-(**Tractor**) -85 L Wooden	
?		Ladder	?	?	Leeds City Fire Brigade	? Simonis-Braun-85 L Wooden	
G653HLS		Light6V	89		Hereford & Worcester Fire Brigade	42 Owen St-Hereford Steyr Puch Pinzgaur-Outreach	
BMN999T		ET	91		Isle of Man Fire & Rescue Service	7 Farrents Way-Castletown Steyr Puch Pinzgaur-Mountain Range	
J125TVN	20	L6R	91		Cleveland County Fire & Rescue-**1996** Cleveland Fire Brigade	7 Seaton Carew Rd-Billingham Steyr Puch Pinzgaur-John Dennis CB	
J126TVN	28	L6R	91		Cleveland County Fire & Rescue-**1996** Cleveland Fire Brigade	3 Trunk Rd-Grangetown Steyr Puch Pinzgaur-John Dennis CB	
H947HAF		C/Unit	91		Cornwall County Fire Brigade	4.1 Station Rd-Truro Talbot Express Turbo-CCFB	
LH9930		Ladder	14	?	LCC London Fire Brigade	? Tilling Stevens—Morris-Magirus-85 L Wooden	
?		Ladder	20	42 ?	Bury St Edmonds Fire Brigade	Bury St Edmonds Tilling Stevens-Magirus-85' L	
?		Ladder	20	42 ?	City of Nottingham	? Tilling Stevens-Braun-85 L Wooden	
?		Ladder	20	42 ?	City of Cardiff	Westgate St-Cardiff Tilling Stevens-Braun- 85 L Wooden	
BB4151		ET	20	35	Newcastle City Fire Brigade	Westgate Rd-Newcastle Tilling Stevens-New World	
BB4150		Ladder	21	42	Newcastle City Fire Brigade	Westgate Rd-Newcastle Tilling Stevens-Braun 87'L	
KB8759	E-1	Ladder	21	43	City of Liverpool	#1 Hatton Gardens-Liverpool-1931 #9 Longmoor Lane-Liverpool-1943 **Ladders re chassied off 1906 Simonis Horse Drawn Tender** Tilling Stevens-Braun- 84'L	
KB8760	E-2	Ladder	21	43	City of Liverpool	#1 Hatton Gardens-Liverpool -1943 Tilling Stevens-Magirus 84'L	
XN8997	ET-1	ET CAV	24	46	LCC London Fire Brigade	Tilling Stevens-LFB	
134PPK		Rec/V	60	84	Surrey County Council Fire Brigade	Brigade Headquarters Thorneycroft Nubian Major 6x6-SFB	
SXT116	1028	CRT	58	77 ?	Liverpool Fire Brigade	Speke Airport Thorneycroft Nubian-Sun	

SXT127	1029	CRT	58	77 ?	Liverpool Fire Brigade	Speke Airport Thorneycroft Nubian-Sun
927SPH		HLL	61	84	Surrey County Council Fire Brigade	Povey Cross Rd-Horley-1974 B10 Povey Cross Rd-Horley-1982 Reserve-1984 -West Sussex Fire Brigade Thorneycroft Nubian **4x4**-SCCFB
928SPH		HLL	61	?	Surrey County Council Fire Brigade	22 Ladymead-Guilford Thorneycroft Nubian **4x4**-SCCFB
929SPH		HLL	61	?	Surrey County Council Fire Brigade	Epsom Fire Station Thorneycroft Nubian **4x4**-SCCFB
KKD685E	1067	CRT	67	?	Liverpool Fire Brigade	Speke Airport Thorneycroft Nubian Major-Merryweather
MKD901F	1074	CRT	68	?	Liverpool Fire Brigade	Speke Airport Thorneycroft Nubian Major-Merryweather
VTG712G		Water Bowser	67	78	Glamorgan County Fire Brigade (Wales)	B1 Sunnyside-Bridgend **Articulated Unit & Trailer** Thorneycroft Nubian-GCFB
VTG713G		Water Bowser	67	78	Glamorgan County Fire Brigade (Wales)	**B1 Sunnyside-Bridgend -? / C1 Pontypridd- ?** **Articulated Unit & Trailer** Thorneycroft Nubian-GCFB
WTG222H		Water Bowser	69	79	Glamorgan County Fire Brigade (Wales)	**B1 Sunnyside-Bridgend-? / A1 Neath-?** **Articulated Unit & Trailer** Thorneycroft Nubian-GCFB
HNY589K		Air-CRT FOT	72	76	Glamorgan County Fire Brigade	B1 Sunnyside-Bridgend Thorneycroft Nubian Major-Carmichael
M794PKJ	109	C/Unit	96		Kent Fire Brigade	S60 Loose Rd-Maidstone Vauxhall Brava-Truckman-Whiteacres **4x4**
M797PKJ	110	C/Unit	96		Kent Fire Brigade	E80 Upper Bridge St-Canterbury Vauxhall Brava-Truckman-Whiteacres **4x4**
M795PKJ	114	C/Unit	96		Kent Fire Brigade	Vauxhall Brava-Truckman-Whiteacres **4x4**
M796PKJ	115	C/Unit	96		Kent Fire Brigade	N43 Watling St-Rochester-Medway Vauxhall Brava-Truckman-Whiteacres **4x4**
OUV290R	FT-10	FOT	77	91	GLC London Fire Brigade	E30 High St-Eltham Unipower R42-Chubb

Delivered in 1961 to the Surrey County Council, this Guilford-based Thorneycroft Nubian Hose Layer 928SPH was one of three which would serve the brigade. In 1974 boundary changes would take the Horley based example to West Sussex control leaving this example and one at Epsom still under Surrey control. All the appliances had the added advantage of having four wheel drive capability.
Keith Wardell collection

ABBREVIATIONS

TYPE	EXPLANATION OF ABBREVIATION	REMARKS
ACCU	Accident Unit	Similar to Emergency/Rescue Tender
AMB	Ambulance	Full Paramedic Accident/Rescue capibility
ALP	Aerial Ladder Platform/ 90' Or 110' Height	Bronto Skylift **28-2TI** (29.5M) **33-2TI** & **ST300-S**(31.5M) **ST240-S** (25.5M)**ST290-S** (31 M)
Argocat	Argocat	6 Wheel Drive off road vehicle
BAT	Breathing Apparatus Tender	Can service Breathing Apparatus sets on scene
BL/RECV	Breakdown or Recovery Tender/Lorry	
B/WRC	Bulk Water Carrier	Large Water Carrier
CAV	Canteen Van	Salvation Army or Brigade run.
CIU	Chemical Incident Unit	Carries full Decontamination/Showering facilities.
CPL	Compact Platform Ladder	Same as **APL**
CRT	Crash Rescue Tender	Foam/Water Capibility
CRU	Cliff Rescue Unit/Tender	Carry's line's/winches/stretcher's
CSU	Command Support Unit	Same as Control Unit-normally smaller
CU/COMMU	Control Unit/Command Unit	Attends 5+ Pump Fire/Incident's
DCU	Damage Control Unit	Salvage/Drying/Security equipment
DU	Decontamination Unit	Attends Radioactive/Chemical Incident's
EP	Emergency Pump's	Green Goddess. Auxillary Fire Service machines.
ERA	Emergency Rescue Appliance	Similar to Emergency/Rescue Tender
ESU	Emergency Support Unit	Similar to **HRT/MRT/RES/U** etc
ET	Emergency Tender	Carries winches/spreader's/cutting gear inc **Holmatro/Zumro/Turfor/Kango/Clan Lukas**
FCU	Forward Control Unit	Can be mounted on a 4x4 chassis.
FOC	Foam Carrier/Tanker	Bulk Foam Carrier
FBT	Fire Boat	
F/HL	Foam Hose Layer	Combination Vehicle
FIU	Fire Investigation Unit	Carries fire investigators to incidents/Equipment
FOT	Foam Tender	Some can be in pod form
FPU	Fire Prevention Unit	Attends after the incident is over.
F/SALV	Foam/Salvage Tender	Machine with dual role.
H/FOT	Hose Layer/Foam Tender	Machine with dual role.
Hi-ex FT	High Expansion Foam Tender	Carries Foam making materials.
HLL	Hose Laying Lorry	Contains approx 3 miles of hose on rack's
HP	Hydraulic Platform	**SS50**(50') **SS65**(65') **SS70**(70') **SS85**(85') **SS220**(77') **SS263**(91') **SS300**(103') **Orbitor** booms 72'
HoseRT	Hose Reel Tender	Term not used today/replaced by WRT
HRT	Heavy Rescue Tender	Same as **ET / MRT / RES/ISU**

ISU	Incident Support Unit	Same as **ET/MRT** /carries extra salvage/chemical equipment
L2P	Light 2wheel Drive Vehicle with Pump	Ford Transit/Sherpa Freight Rover etc
L4P/L6P	Light 4/6wheel Drive Vehicle with Pump	Land Rover/Range Rover/Pinzgaur/Uni-mog etc
L4T	Light 4Wheel Drive Vehicle with Hose reel	Land Rover/Austin Gypsey etc
L4V	Light 4wheel Drive Vehicle	Land Rover/Pinzgaur etc
LU	Lighting Unit	Rare most **WRL/WRT** have stem mast's.
MRT	Major Rescue Tender	Similar to Emergency/Rescue Tenders
Mini WRT	Mini Water Tender	WRT on smaller chasis
MW	Mobile Workshops	Often has towing facility.
OSU	Operational Support Unit	Same as **ET / MRT / RES/SU / HRT / ISU**
PUMP	Pump	Pump with 30'/35' extension ladder.
PE	Pump Escape	Pump with 50' wheeled ladder.
PHP	Pump Hydraulic Platform	Pump with 50'/60' Simon platform.
PL	Pump Ladder	Pump with 45' extension ladder.
P/FOT	Pump Foam Tender	Pump with foam making capibility/monitor.
PM	Prime Mover/Pod System	Pod's of all type's **CU/CIU/REST/FOT**etc.
PRL	Pump Rescue Ladder	Same as **WRL/R**
RAV	Road Accident Vehicle	Similar to Emergency/Rescue Tender
RES/SU	Rescue Support Unit	Same as **REST/Possibly fitted HIAB/Paflinger crane**
REST	Rescue Tender	Carry same equipment as **ET/MRT** but in smaller form.
RIV	Rapid Intervention Vehicle	First strike vehicle/Rescue capibility
RRU	Road Rescue Unit	Similar to Rescue Tender
SALV	Salvage Tender	Salvage only/Sheets/Driers/Vacums etc
SCOHR	Scoosher	Scottish slang term for 'Water Pistol'. A Scottish Tele boomed appliance.
SEA/EQT	Sea Equipment Tender	Carries Boat and equipment relevent to maritime rescue.
SIMTR	Simoniter	Pump with a Simon 15m Telescopic Boom.
SRV	Special Rescue Vehicle	Similar to Emergency/Rescue Tender
TL	Turntable Ladder	100' / 125' / 150' /
TLP	Turntable Ladder Pump	1,000 GPM Pump fitted.
TSU	Technical Support Unit	Similar to Emergency/Rescue Tender
WRA	Water Appliance	Same as the **WRT.**
WRU	Water Relay Unit	Appliance with added hose and heavy pumping capacity.
WRC	Water Carrier/Bowser	5,000 Gallon's.Can be fitted with 1,000 gp.
WRL	Water Ladder	**WRT** with 45' extension ladder.
WRL/R	Water Ladder/Rescue	as above. Also rescue equipment carried.
WRT	Water Tender	**WRT** with 30/35' extension ladder.
WRT/E	Water Tender/Escape	**WRT** with 35/50' wheeled escape ladder.
WRT/L	Water Tender/Ladder	**WRT** with 35'/45' extension ladder.
WRT/R	Water Tender/Rescue	As **WRL/R** but with 35' extension ladder.

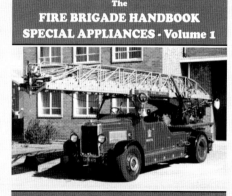